It Was Never About the Cake

A Middle-Aged Woman's Journey of Overcoming an Eating Disorder and Discovering Her Best Self

Teresa Schmitz

It Was Never About the Cake
© 2022 by Teresa Schmitz

Published with help from 100X Publishing
Olympia, Washington | www.kristadunk.com/100xPublishing

This title is also available in Kindle format.

ISBN: 978-1-7339893-4-3

Headshot on back of book by: Photography by Melissa Marie
Book cover design by: Noel Sellon
My Best Self Yet company logo design by: Ariana Rose Graphics

Dedication

This book is dedicated to all those who have faced or are facing an eating disorder and/or body image issues. There is hope in the healing.

You can become your best self too.

Contents

Foreword

By Angie Michel

It's not easy to tell your story. Like all things vulnerable, it takes abandon, guts and faith. To do it after years of believing your experience doesn't matter—that *you* don't matter—is a sign of healing. A scar unconcealed, it is a testament to self-acceptance, respect and hard-earned progress.

And it is what you have in your hands now.

In *It Was Never About the Cake*, Teresa Schmitz lays bare her experience of eating disorder illness and recovery, letting us in on the inner landscape of a widely misunderstood mental health issue. Through poignant journals and self-reflections, we meet the parts of Teresa once smothered in shame—the ones that needed care. We see the factors that threatened to keep her sick and those that helped her heal. We feel her fears and her joys as we follow her path away from her eating disorder toward a fuller and richer life.

I count myself lucky to have been among the earliest public audiences to Teresa's story. Our paths first crossed in my work inbox when she reached out about The Emily Program's *Peace Meal* podcast, a show I manage as part of my job at the eating disorder treatment organization. Episodes regularly feature guests in eating disorder recovery, those who have been through the chaos of these cruel, confusing illnesses and fought for something more. These people are living out a reality that sometimes seems too good to be true: recovery is possible. It is possible and it is worth it. Teresa was interested in sharing her story if it could help one other person, and of course I knew it would.

Nearly 30 million people in the United States will experience an eating disorder in their lifetime—9% of the population.[1] Yet despite the widespread prevalence of these illnesses, our public understanding is still largely informed by the stereotype of a teenage girl with anorexia or bulimia. This is neither Teresa's story, nor the story of most people with eating disorders, those whose identities, experiences and illnesses differ from mainstream portrayals. These mental conditions have no one "look," and they leave no part of the population untouched. Cutting across age, size, gender, race, ethnicity, ability, and class categories, they can and do affect people of all kinds. The lived experiences of eating disorders are as diverse as people themselves, and to truly understand and appreciate these differences, we need to hear voices from all sides.

Eating disorders come with sticky myths, ones that say they're a *choice* or a matter of *willpower*. They're often chalked up to behavior problems with an easy fix: "just eat" or "just eat less." But eating disorders are not decisions. People don't choose one to lose weight or gain attention. They don't get them because they can or cannot "control themselves" around food. Eating disorders are complex, brain-based illnesses influenced by biological, psychological and social components. It is likely that they emerge when a genetic predisposition is triggered by a complex combination of other factors. Once triggered, their hold is fierce.

While it seems like eating disorders are all about the food—eating too much, not eating enough—the illnesses hijack all aspects of a person's life. They disconnect people from their bodies and themselves, wreaking havoc on relationships, quality of life and physical, mental and emotional health. The second-deadliest of all mental illnesses, eating disorders kill one American every 52 minutes.[2]

Among the trickiest eating disorder symptoms is thinking you're not sick at all, or at least not *sick enough*. It is common for people with these illnesses

---

[1]   Deloitte Access Economics. *The Social and Economic Cost of Eating Disorders in the United States of America: A Report for the Strategic Training Initiative for the Prevention of Eating Disorders and the Academy for Eating Disorders.* June 2020. Available at: https://www.hsph.harvard.edu/striped/report-economic-costs-of-eating-disorders

[2]   Deloitte Access Economics. *The Social and Economic Cost of Eating Disorders in the United States of America.*

to believe their condition isn't valid—that they made it up or it's somehow their fault. For those with binge eating disorder (BED), the misinformed idea that bingeing is simply overeating (and *haven't we all overeaten before?*) is among the cultural forces that invalidate a complex and serious illness. Stories like Teresa's remind us that BED is very real. It's also very treatable.

Stigma is one of the key reasons why the large majority of people with eating disorders don't get help. To help combat this stigma, we must listen and learn from those who experience the illnesses firsthand. Here, Teresa has given us a gift toward that end. A much-needed contribution to the eating disorder library, her powerful memoir is a resource for those treating or supporting those with these illnesses and a guiding star for those still in the darkness.

My respect for Teresa has only deepened since she shared her story on *Peace Meal*. Her continued growth is inspiring and her writing compassionate, true and infinitely more impressive than any external labels that once mistakenly defined her. In the pages that follow, I think you'll see your own humanness in the many layers of Teresa's truth. As you witness her stand firmer in her worthiness, may you, too, settle deep in yours.

—Angie Michel

Preface

In my 40s, at the height of my eating disorder and body image issues, I was slowly killing myself. Sadly, society equates an eating disorder with teenage girls. Most people do not and would not consider equating an eating disorder with middle-aged women. That almost seems to be an oxymoron of sorts, yet I am living proof of that oxymoron. I was diagnosed with my own eating disorder just three weeks shy of my 46th birthday. I would proudly declare my recovered status nearly three years later, almost to the date.

To further add to the generalizations society makes when it comes to eating disorders is that it is all about anorexia. That too is far from the truth. In fact, my diagnosis of binge eating disorder is far more common than anorexia. And having binge eating disorder does not necessarily equate to someone who is obese or overweight. As much as society likes to generalize about what eating disorders "look like," there is no way to tell if someone has an eating disorder. Many think an eating disorder means someone "just" doesn't know how to eat enough or when to stop. Again, so far from the truth. It actually has nothing to do with the food, and yet everything to do with the food. It's that complicated! After all, it is a mental health disorder; willpower alone can't overcome it.

When I searched for middle-aged women recovery stories to read for inspiration after my own diagnosis, I found most stories were from those diagnosed as teenagers or young adults. Same with social media accounts claiming their own eating disorder recovery. Only a small handful of books for middle-aged women (looking for successful recovery stories of those her age) exist. I know because I searched and searched. At times, I felt that recovery was not possible for someone at my age (remember the saying, "You can't teach an old dog new tricks"?), and the lack of books was more evidence. It made me feel alone.

Because of this, I vowed to help at least one other middle-aged woman know she is not alone. Although vulnerable, speaking out about my story after I had been in recovery for a bit was important to me. Some who knew me most of my life had no idea I had recovered from an eating disorder or that I had even been diagnosed. Telling my story started by drafting this book, and then appearing as a guest on a podcast called *Peace Meal* hosted by The Emily Program. It started a beautiful journey of mine that I hope becomes a movement of sorts.

Middle-aged women need to know they matter in the recovery journey; they are capable of recovering, and we need them to write and share their stories too. We are out there. We are warriors, just like those at younger ages who have recovered. It may not seem like it when you search at your local library or online for positive middle-aged recovery warriors like I did, so my goal is that this story of mine gives you hope. Have hope that you, too, can recover and know you are not alone. Hope that you too will find all the gifts your eating disorder diagnosis has given you.

XO,

Teresa

Note: While most names are the true names of the individuals in this memoir, a few names were changed to protect the identity of some individuals.

Diagnosis

"You are not a project that needs fixin'."
—Jen Nelson, LPCC

 **If you** think about it, God (or the universe if you don't believe in God) has a way of giving you gifts in the most peculiar of situations. We may not realize it at the time. Sometimes, we need to be far removed from the situation (i.e., years) to realize the gift or gifts that we received. That was the case of my eating disorder diagnosis. It was not until I was far into recovery that I would realize the gifts that God had blessed me with when giving me an eating disorder diagnosis at mid-life.

As I mentioned (in the Preface), at the height of my eating disorder and body image issues, I was slowly killing myself. I didn't see it that way, even though the doctors complimented me when I lost weight in between visits and at the same time told me I had an unhealthy relationship with food. One doctor even asked if I would keep my life the same if I knew the stress of my life and job would kill me in ten years. Even so, I didn't see my eating disorder or my lifestyle as a problem. My eating disorder was a way to cope with all the stressors in my life and my lifestyle was a way to show the world I was worthy. Because deep inside, my eating disorder had made me believe that I was unworthy.

For many years, my identity was my job title. Since I didn't feel good enough as a mom when my kids were younger (my own mom was "better" because she was a stay-at-home mom), I poured my identity into my job title. My worth was equated to the size of my paycheck and how much recognition I received at work. I spent years accumulating stuff – more projects, more people to manage, more recognition for exceeding expectations year over year, more material things for our home – all to define my own self-worth. I soon surpassed my husband and became the breadwinner of our family. I thought I was going places. Then, over the course of three years, my "worth" from my job was unraveling, and the only thing to fall back on (mom role) had already "decreased" in value. My oldest child was now an adult and my youngest was soon there himself. I thought I had nothing left to define me. My fallback was gone.

In a middle-aged woman's body, seeing my value stripped away, happened (in what felt like) overnight. Looking at my body evoked shame. My internal world had collapsed. I'd spent years trying to control everything in front of me...every last detail. And then came a diagnosis that felt like a blow to everything I had worked so hard to secure.

*****

I vividly recall the day when I was diagnosed with my eating disorder. It was a Friday; Friday, October 27, 2017, to be exact. I was just 21 days shy of turning 46. I had an appointment at 9:00 a.m. at The Emily Program on Como Avenue off Highway 280 in St Paul, Minnesota, that day. A light snow was falling that morning. I took the morning off from work and told my boss, who I'd been reporting to for just over two months, that I had a doctor appointment. Looking back, it would have been best to have taken the whole day off, but at the time, I wasn't so good about taking care of myself, especially when it meant missing work and setting healthy boundaries. I got this work ethic from my dad, but more on that later.

About two weeks prior to this diagnosis, I was in a therapy session with my then-therapist, Mari (rhymes with Ferrari, as she told me when I first started seeing her nearly seven months prior). During that session, she said she felt I had an unhealthy relationship with food and some body image issues. She mentioned depression too, which was on top of the generalized anxiety that was diagnosed when I initially started seeing her in early March 2017. She told me I should call my physician about the depression to be advised about whether medication made sense. She also told me to seek out The Emily Program for an assessment for the food and body image issues.

"I just can't seem to lose weight. No one loves larger bodies. I eat raw cookie dough in secret after eating breakfast on the way into the office. It takes the edge off," I would tell her. What's wrong with that? And yet, I knew she knew a thing or two about eating disorders herself, as it once came up in a therapy session that she suffered from bulimia at one point in her life.

This would not be the first time a provider mentioned my relationship with food. Back in 2011, my general practitioner prescribed for me to go on a diet unfortunately. "A diet like Weight Watchers is a good option," she would say. "You don't want to die young of a heart attack like your dad," she would continue. When I returned three months later to see how much weight I had lost, I had actually gained a little. This doctor shamed me about my weight and terrified me about dying young like my father, so I ate for comfort that evening and dieted the next morning.

At the end of my follow-up appointment, she referred me to a therapist, as she felt I had an unhealthy relationship with food. At the time, I had no idea what this meant and honestly thought I had done something wrong. *There is something wrong with me since I gained weight and disappointed her.* If only my provider had been more informed to refer me to an eating disorder treatment program, then I would have received the help I needed six years earlier. And by the way, telling a person with an eating disorder they need to lose weight is the worst thing you can say to them. It's like telling a breast cancer patient they are at fault for their diagnosis.

What's really unfortunate, is that this same doctor became the director of my health care provider's weight loss program. Five years later in 2016, I would follow her and join her program to lose weight. More on this later, but she told me for a second time that I had an unhealthy relationship with food during that time. This was all after I had dropped a significant amount of weight by taking appetite suppressants under her care. I kept on the appetite suppressant medication the entire time she kept questioning my relationship with food. The red flags were all there. I only wish our medical doctors were more trained on how to spot an eating disorder and refer patients to an eating disorder specific program outrightly.

After my appointment with Mari in mid-October 2017, I looked up The Emily Program online. I wasn't sure any of it applied to me, and yet I found the courage to call. They had a long wait time for an intake assessment at the Woodbury location, so they scheduled me at the Como location right away. The whole time I kept thinking *I don't have a problem. I just can't seem to lose weight on my own, am fat, eat when I am not even hungry and eat in secret. I am stressed from my job. What's so wrong with that?* Most of my former Weight Watcher dieters would say the same thing when they saw a gain on the scale. It was a letdown. I am a failure at losing weight was what I was thinking.

On the flip side, it was a score when you could go on a binge after a "successful" Weight Watchers weigh-in; a weigh-in that included a gold star and a round of applause from the group. I remember dreaming of the binge that was about to happen when that scale showed a loss. I would dream of cheeseburgers, French fries, chips, cookies, popcorn, cake, or Diet Coke. It was always about diet soda when on the Weight Watchers plan, because it was 0 points, and I could drink as much as I wanted, sometimes 32-64 oz in a day. I deserved a buffet of food for all the restricting I did the week before to obtain that approval from the WW staff and the group at large, right? I would eat until beyond full, and then search for more in private later. This binge would all take place after coming home and writing the number I weighed on a blank piece of paper in a notebook. Then, I had my very impressionable teenage daughter, Kaitlyn, take a photo of me displaying that number.

Food…it was always on my mind. *What am I going to have for lunch? Let's go out for dinner tonight. I deserve it, as I've had a long day at work* or *my boss is stressing me out. Then, when we get home, let me binge on popcorn, chips, cake, cookies, and whatever else I can eat when the kids are in bed and Dale,* my husband, *is off at work. Let me hide "my food" behind other containers in the cupboards and fridge and get mad when someone else ate "my food." It was mine. Don't they know I was going to escape with that later tonight? It had my name written all over it, and I've been dreaming about the quick fix and escape since the 9:00 a.m. meeting with my boss.*

Back to the day I was diagnosed with my eating disorder. I signed in at the front desk nearly 30 minutes before my Friday appointment. I was given a ton of paperwork to complete, which included a variety of assessments.

How often do you eat more than what others would consider normal? How often have you weighed yourself in the last seven days? How often do you… all kinds of questions. I finished the paperwork at the table they had me sit at and turned it in at the front desk. Then, I headed to the bathroom. There was a note about flushing posted on the toilet; a note that would only make sense when I started eating disorder treatment.

Back in the waiting room, I noticed the tables were all covered with jigsaw puzzles. I arrived well in advance of my appointment because I wasn't sure about the snowy road conditions and the route was one I hadn't travelled during rush hour before. To kill the time, I absently read a Suze Orman article in a *Money* magazine I'd brought with me. I don't remember any of what I read. I put the magazine down and sat in silence, wondering what was ahead of me.

A young girl checked in with her mat for yoga, and she and the woman at the front desk discussed her co-pay. Another young girl checked in and sat down nearby. She started working on the puzzle on the table in front of her. I remember thinking *if only I could relax and do a puzzle. I love puzzles. She looks like she is totally enjoying herself over there.*

A short time later, the young girl doing the puzzle was called back. The therapist or dietitian picking her up made small talk, asking her how she was doing and what puzzle she was working on. The therapist or dietitian was so kind and friendly I thought. Another young girl came up from the lower level and stopped at the front desk. She was upset when asking about the package her mom mailed her, as she had not yet received it. Her mom told her she sent it, but it did not have a tracking number, so there was no saying where the package was at this point. All I knew was that this girl really wanted her package from home. My heart ached for her. And her mom.

Finally, my time of waiting was up. Jessica called me back. "Teresa?" she said, as if wondering if that was me. "My name is Jessica. I am filling in for Julie, one of the intake therapists who is out sick today." Jessica led me back to her office that overlooked the parking lot in the back. I could see the snow sticking to the grass as I sat in the chair. After telling me that she reviewed the assessments I took, she started asking a lot of questions.

"What brought you here? What was your childhood like? How close are you with your mom? Dad? Siblings? What would it feel like if you gained five pounds? What would it feel like if you never lost weight again? How do you view your body?" We spent an hour and a half together. The tears just kept flowing. I kept apologizing for crying. Jessica kept telling me that most patients say the same thing and there was no reason to apologize.

At the end of our conversation, she told me I had binge eating disorder and that I needed Intensive Outpatient Programming (IOP for short). I had not heard of binge eating disorder before. My extent of eating disorder knowledge was anorexia and bulimia. I knew what those meant in general, and yet had not really heard of binge eating disorder. She said they were starting up programming in Woodbury and that it was very similar to the one at the Como location. You either meet from 9:00-noon or 5:00-8:00 p.m. It was four days a week. *Four days a week? What? I can't do all of that. That's too much. I've got too much going on. I work. I have a life. Don't you know?*

Looking back, this was the first acknowledgment of my eating disorder throwing a fit. The eating disorder would fight against everything related to recovery, saying things like, "You don't need treatment, you need me to survive." In hindsight, this was the best news I had received in a long time. My life was spinning out of control, and I thought *if only I'd lose more weight, I wouldn't be depressed, I could love my body and I'd be more confident.* This of course wasn't true, yet it was where I was at in my journey.

I drove home in the cold and snow and stopped at the McDonald's drive thru on the way home to escape the news I'd just heard. *How can I have an eating disorder? I must have answered a couple questions incorrectly or she heard me wrong when we were talking about my life.* It couldn't be. I just needed something to numb the pain, and food was the cure. I felt so alone, so ashamed. *How could you let this happen? If only you would have learned something when on the appetite suppressant prescribed in 2016, you wouldn't be this way right now.* Only now do I realize that my eating disorder (often referred to as "Ed" by many with an eating disorder) was putting on one big, fat shame shit-fest as I went through the drive-thru.

I felt even more alone when I told my husband later that day at home. He was sitting at the kitchen table, attempting to wake up with a cup of coffee after working the night shift. I told him I needed a hug because I was just diagnosed with binge eating disorder. He asked me what I needed from him. I responded, "Nothing," as I didn't really know what I needed at that time. Quite honestly, it was a typical response for me, as I didn't ask for help. In actuality, I was numb. I was ashamed. I felt so alone. Like a failure. *I have a good job, make good money, have two beautiful children and I can't get my shit together when it comes to food. What is wrong with me?*

It took a lot of courage to tell my husband. The story I made up in my head was that he isn't one who seeks out therapy for himself, so he will think I am looking for an excuse. The voice in my head got louder and louder: *You are just looking for an excuse for being fat. We Schmitz's don't roll like that.* Louder, louder, louder.

I felt even more ashamed after that interaction. Only in programming would I learn about "Dear Man" (a framework for having assertive conversations that I will provide details on later) and being assertive in telling Dale, my husband, and others what I really needed. That would take time and practice. And I'd get there eventually. Being assertive or confronting anyone, especially my husband, wasn't anything remotely possible at this point in my life. You kept everything inside and ate your feelings with soothing food later. Numb. *I'll just numb later and escape the conflict now.* Ed was always with me in these early days, dictating my every move without my awareness. I had no idea this *wasn't* my voice. It would take lots of therapy to discover that these stories, these words, were all coming from Ed.

Looking back on this diagnosis and the weeks leading up to it, my authentic self seemed to be on to something. I just didn't know it. Just 40 days before my diagnosis, I sat in my bedroom in my glider rocking chair, the one we still had from when I was first pregnant with Kaitlyn, my oldest. It's green and does not go at all with the paint on the bedroom walls. It provides a sense of comfort, a sense of familiarity, a sense of simpler times. The following was my journal entry on Sunday, 9/17/17 at 2:59 pm:

> *"The sun shines in on the carpet, with a gentle breeze, making the shadows of the leaves sway along the carpet. A distant motorcycle is heard from Hwy 61. Now the blow of a loud train horn as*

*it chugs down the tracks. The little bird chirps ever so quietly. I
imagine it is a small bird, yellow, with a tiny beak. The windows
are open and life feels good. It feels good in this moment because I
am in tune with my outdoor surroundings while in the comfort of
my green glider rocker."*

Later in this same journal entry, I say:

*"Sometimes you are forced to make a change which is for the best
in the long haul. I feel like a change is about a year or two away."*

At this point in time, I would not know the magnitude of the change that
was coming in just a matter of days, not years. I was so focused on losing
weight and changing my body leading up to my diagnosis. On Sunday,
October 15th, we celebrated the 11-year anniversary of my dad's passing at
my mom's church. He was the Mass intention for the 6:30 p.m. Mass that
Sunday night. My oldest sister came, along with her husband, her oldest
daughter and her granddaughter. My third sister also came, along with her
husband and two adult children. My son joined me. It was a celebration for
my dad and mainly a show of support for my mom, and yet I was comparing
my weight to one of my sisters. I'd later journal that same night:

*"Why can't I lose weight for good and take care of my health like
she is? . . . I chase after the latest diet craze and get mad when I
gain it all back and then some. Why can't I lose for good? What's
holding me back?"*

And then more thoughts in my journal the next day:

*"Why can't you just be happy? . . . I hate how I am right now.
Resentful. Mean to myself. Unkind. Jealous. Ick. Ick. Ick. Help
me, Lord. This is madness. It's like I can't be kind."*

It's so sad to know I spent years beating myself up (or shall I say Ed beat
me up) after some failed diet, always thinking I needed to change. Little
did I know this was an Eating Disorder voice that said, "I am not good

enough." It's the same voice I heard at the age of seven. To understand where this all comes from, I'd spend over two years peeling back the layers of my childhood in therapy at The Emily Program.

The Gift of Forgiveness

"Your wounds are not likely your fault,
but your healing is your responsibility."
—Jen Nelson, LPCC

 A very normal, almost ideal, childhood was most likely how many would describe mine when looking in from the outside. From the outside, we had ourselves on our best. My name Teresa meant "little flower" my mom told me. My parents were married, not divorced like the parents of my first-grade best friend. Her parents got divorced in about the third grade, and I felt sad for her. *Why do parents divorce?* This was the late 1970's when the divorce rate was not anywhere close to what it is today. It seemed foreign to me back then.

My dad had a good job as a research physicist at 3M, a major Fortune 500 company in Minnesota. He would eventually obtain secret security clearance because of the work he and his team were doing in collaboration with the Air Force and US Government around airplanes. He walked nearly two miles one way to work most days from our house that was near the high school on the east side of St. Paul. My mom packed his lunch in a brown paper bag every work day. He called home every day at lunch time to see how she was doing. We always knew it was dad on the other end, as she always responded, "Oh, I'm doing…" when he asked how she was doing in that first greeting.

My dad made decent money – enough for our family of six to survive on his income alone. He plowed the sidewalk with his snowblower and did the same for some elderly neighbors' driveways in the alley when he first got a snowblower. He tinkered in the garage with wood and built us bookcases, shelves and record player/stereo holders that would house all our 80's vinyl records (*Thriller* from Michael Jackson, *The Greatest Hits* from REO Speedwagon, Chicago and so many more). He could fix just about anything in that garage.

My mom stayed home with us four girls (I was the youngest). She occasionally had a job. One time, she did daycare in our home...until she had a parent taking advantage of her, and the woman's child was soon eating dinner with us most nights. That put an end to her daycare in our home. Mom was President of the PTO (Parent Teacher Organization) when I was in elementary school. She made homemade birthday treats; her chocolate chip bars were a usual favorite to bring. In fact, one year she was on a business trip with my dad in Boston, so her parents were at the house taking care of us. It was my birthday and Mom was not home to make those chocolate chip bars. Grandma Jingles (what we called her because she had a tiger eye ring that jingled on her finger when she moved her hands) could not make them the same way. I pouted about this, but Grandma tried her best.

My mom helped students in my class who struggled with their English. She was a staple at the elementary school through all the years of us attending. The teachers, school secretary, principal, kids in many different classrooms, and even the janitors, all knew her by her first name. Thankfully, everyone knew how to pronounce our last name at the school. Hardly anyone got our last name right, especially the solicitors calling on the phone or showing up at the door to sell us the latest carpet shampoo or Encyclopedia subscription.

When I was in the fourth grade, the school district proposed to close our elementary school for lack of enrollment. My mom fought hard to "Save the Sharks" (our school nickname was the Sharks). She even had drawstring bags made up for the occasion and t-shirts we could wear to the district meeting. All that hard effort paid off when the school board voted to leave our school open. The school would go on to thrive for years, and finally closed down in 2012, which was about 30 years later.

We had a station wagon…the kind where the third row faced backwards and the window rolled down only halfway. In the third row was where my third-oldest sister and I would sit, because we were the youngest of the family. My other two sisters rode in the middle seats, with our dog Clancey sandwiched in between. We proudly named this station wagon "The Family Plan Unit."

We ate home cooked dinners my mom prepared for us around the kitchen table every night. We had a family dog. We had pet fish. Two of my sisters had guinea pigs for a while. My dad flooded our backyard for a skating rink a few years in a row. We had a garden in the back of our yard by the alley and garage that would grow cucumbers, carrots, lettuce, tomatoes, rhubarb, and pumpkins each year. One year we had a giant pumpkin that grew to nearly three feet in circumference. When we were gone to the lake, it was smashed by some neighborhood boys who wanted to cause a little trouble now and then. The next year, we got another big pumpkin to grow, and when it dropped and broke after being picked from the garden, my fix-it dad nailed the pieces back together! As I said, he could fix just about anything. At least that is how it looked from the outside.

We travelled to my grandparents' home on Lake Miltona, two and a half hours away, most weekends in the summer as a family in our "Family Plan Unit." My dad would take my third-oldest sister and I out fishing in my Grandpa Dean's Lund boat. "Set the hook," he would holler, as we tried to reel in the big fish on our bobber pole. Often, we would have no fish on the end of the pole when we reeled it all the way in…just an empty hook where a worm once curved itself around. When we came up empty-handed, my dad would once again remind us that we needed to set the hook. When we moved to another spot on the lake, he would open up the motor and speed across the lake as I yelled, "Slow down!" as loud as I could. My dad would eventually get his own boat, and we would rent a cabin up north at a different lake for a week one summer, something that really bothered my grandparents. "What's wrong with our lake?" they would say.

On Sundays, we went to the Catholic church across the street from our elementary school. My mom was really involved as a Eucharistic Minister and Lector by the time I got into high school. I would wear a dress and knee-high socks to church when in elementary school. These socks would come in handy when I had a runny nose and the only thing available was either my dad's hanky (eew) or my socks. The socks won out every time! We attended CCD classes (like Bible study or Faith Formation classes) on Wednesday nights. Everyone knew my mom, and once again, they knew how to pronounce our last name!

Life seemed so "ideal" looking in from the street. We put on a good show and hid everything behind those four walls of the little house on Fremont in the 1970's and early 1980's. What people on the outside didn't know was that my dad used alcohol, porn and work to numb. You wouldn't know that from the outside; it was our family secret. We had all the previously mentioned things going for us from the outside. Life looked ideal from the outside when the inside was falling apart. We weren't a pumpkin who could be nailed back together when broken into pieces.

I first started to notice the little things. At the age of seven, I recall a Christmas program we were going to put on for our parents at school. We would sing "Up on the Housetop" and turn around to wiggle our cotton-ball butts when we sang the words "Ho Ho Ho." My dad wasn't there. Only my mom was there in the audience. My mom said my dad had to work and couldn't come. I wanted my dad there.

Then there was the third grade when I was in the spelling bee. I went neck and neck with my best friend from first grade. We were the best of friends until about fifth grade when we each started hanging out with other girls. She would eventually hang out with the kids who smoked pot in ninth grade, while I continued to be a bookworm and hang out with the nerds. We were the last two contestants standing when we had each spelled our last third-grade words correctly. They needed to move on to the fourth-grade words now. We did not receive these words in advance to study. They needed to decide who would win, and it would all come down to the word "jerk." My best friend spelled her word correctly, so I was up next. "Spell the word jerk," the teacher said. "J-U-R-K," I replied. Wrong. It's spelled J-E-R-K.

I remember being disappointed as my friend beat me and I didn't win it all. My dad did not attend this event either, and I don't recall the excuse, as this one was in the evening hours. I will not ever forget what my mom said to me afterwards. It sticks with me to this day. "I thought you'd get that for sure.

It sounds so much like the beginning of our last name and rhymes with it – Verk. Jerk.," she would say. Feeling like I let her down was unbearable, on top of feeling like I wasn't good enough for my dad to attend my event. Not good enough in first grade when dad didn't show to my Christmas concert, and now not even in a third-grade spelling bee.

About this same timeframe, I remember attending my dad's softball games in the summer months at Tartan Park, a park that was exclusive to 3M employees and their families. It was where my dad took me out to eat to celebrate my 4.0 GPA after my first year of college. It was also where I would later host my wedding reception at the golf course's clubhouse. Back in the late 1970's, we would watch my dad play softball with a bunch of younger men from work. One was named Willie, and they called him the birdman since he liked to look for birds. Maybe these men weren't younger than my dad, they only seemed like it, as most of them did not have a wife and four kids sitting there watching them. After the games, we would go hang out at the pavilion and watch my dad drink the night away on the picnic tables. Then, we would all bundle into "The Family Plan Unit" and drive the nearly 12 miles home. It was like playing Russian Roulette with your entire family, yet he never got pulled over, and we thankfully never ended up in a ditch.

What started off as "not good enough" would turn into full-fledged perfectionism that would eat me up as the years progressed. By junior high school, everything I was wearing would have to match. I had to get an A or better in everything I did in school. I had to be the first chair of the clarinets in the band. I had to have the perfect hair. Later, as an adult, I had to get a 4.0 in college to get my dad's approval. I would have to get the perfect title (QA Manager) at work, even if it meant I let my life at home and my health go. All external things to make it look like we had our shit together at home.

My dad started to isolate himself in the basement of our home to numb after a hard day at work. I started watching hockey, our MN North Stars home team, in third grade just so I could get a little time with my dad. He worked long hours and never called in sick. He would take two weeks off over the Christmas and New Year's holidays to spend time with us. It almost felt like he was making up for the lack of attending any school events or being around much during the other 50 weeks of the year. He was physically there, yet emotionally empty.

He would betray my mom during their marriage, most of which I did not realize until much later in my life. The ultimate betrayal was when I was a senior in high school. My mom shared the details of that betrayal with me at the time it happened and told me not to tell my dad that I knew. I wanted to disown my own father. I wanted my mom to divorce him. I felt ashamed. I felt dirty. I felt so alone. It was a family secret of ours that most people don't know anything about.

I didn't want to talk to my father at the time. It was awkward. I knew about everything, and yet he didn't know I knew. The only child left living at home when all of this happened, it got awkward at times. My mom was working part time in the late afternoons, so if my dad got home from work before she did, I was alone in the house with him. My mom would come home and ask me if Dad drank while she was gone. Of course I heard him "quietly" open the cupboard and clink the Windsor bottle against another bottle in the cupboard. I'd hear the ice cubes clank into the glass and the burst of fizz from the two-liter bottle of Diet Coke being opened. *Do I really have to be the one who tells you all of this? Do you really have to ask?* I would think every time.

It's not until my therapy time during eating disorder treatment when I would come to understand how my dad never had a chance to learn healthy coping skills when he was younger, and that he, too, suffered from untreated mental health issues. He grew up on a farm and slept in a bed with his two older brothers. His parents immigrated to the states from Belgium in search of a better life before they married and settled down to have their children. They had to work hard, and that meant the kids did too. That work ethic and hard outside core was built on that farm in the middle of southwest Minnesota.

My dad was just 17 when he married my mom. They would become parents to my oldest sister just four months later when my dad was still only 17. One month shy of his 27th birthday, I would be born – my parents' youngest child and last. When I joined the world, he was 26, had been married for almost ten years and had four girls. He finished his college degree sometime between the birth of my second and third sisters, and 3M held his job for him while he finished. I don't know how he did it all. It's no wonder he cracked. That's a lot of pressure at such a young age.

He was the first and only child to ever attend and graduate from college in his family. My mom's parents put pressure on him to marry her and get a college education so he could provide. Back then, being unwed and a Catholic was a no-no. In fact, it's why my mom was put up for adoption herself when she was born.

My dad died young – two months shy of his 62nd birthday. He was set to go file for Social Security benefits the morning after he passed. He'd been retired from 3M for nearly eight years, retiring when he was only 54. He received a nice, early buy-out package from them to retire young. He got to enjoy over seven years of retirement before he passed, long enough to see the birth of my two children and become a surrogate father when my husband deployed to Iraq with his Army reserve unit for 15 months in 2003.

The sad thing is, it felt like he was turning things around in his retirement by becoming an awesome grandpa. He was making up for all the lost time he didn't have with us girls. It just wasn't in God's plan for him to see his youngest grandkids grow up. We miss him dearly.

He died without knowing that I knew his "secret" from 17 years prior. I had a hard time letting that go. For years, I wanted to blame everything on him. If only he hadn't been an alcoholic…if only he would have loved me more… if only he wouldn't have made me feel not good enough…

It was so bad that I was growing a chip on my shoulder. And that's when my therapist suggested I write a forgiveness letter to him about seven months into eating disorder treatment. I avoided writing this letter for weeks.

My therapist would ask and I'd say I didn't have time. It wasn't that I didn't have time; it was a way I, too, liked to numb: by avoiding the necessary and eating my feelings instead. The longer I held on to that resentment, the longer I was going to eat and numb. I couldn't escape my eating disorder if I kept avoiding that which was healthy and good for me, so I decided enough was enough. I'd write the letter. Yet, part of me was doing it just to "check it off the list," so to speak, something on a long list of to-dos. The other part of me was doing it to get approval from my therapist. I often chose to do things that would win approval from others. A people pleaser of sorts, it's something very common among those with eating disorders, as is perfectionism.

A full nine months into my eating disorder treatment, the day came. I didn't put that connection together at the time though. Kaitlyn, my daughter, was back at Mankato for her second year of college. Ian, my son, was at home with his girlfriend. It was the end of August. And coincidentally, it was exactly ten months from the day of my diagnosis. I asked Dale if he'd go with me to a spot I'd mentally picked to do what I wanted to do when it was time. He agreed and was very supportive.

A week prior, I wrote the letter to my dad, then read it to my therapist at my appointment. She said I really needed to burn it and let everything go with it, almost like a symbol of letting go of all the resentment I had toward my dad. "It will help with your healing," she said. I was skeptical. I wanted so badly to keep that letter. I worked hard to compose it. In fact, that letter was a "perfect" letter that highlighted my writing skills. What was wrong with reading it from time to time and rehashing the resentment, I would ask my therapist. That made her chuckle a bit before she gave me a look; a look that said *it's time*.

Deep down, I knew it was time to burn the letter. I just don't know if I was mentally prepared to move forward in my recovery. My eating disorder wanted me so badly to stay in a relationship with him and rely on him. This was one way Ed was holding on tight to me. It felt comfortable to numb with food and big gulp-sized sodas. It's only when the shame shit-fest happened a bit later when the hangover would start.

I grabbed my letter and electric lighter/fire starter we used to start our backyard family bonfires. It was a dry, windy and warm August day, ten months to the day from when I was diagnosed. The sun was beating down hard as the wind blew. Dale and I got in my car and drove the few blocks up to the scenic overlook in our neighborhood. We got out of the car and were greeted with a swarm of Monarch butterflies clinging to the purple cone flowers on the entrance of the trail leading to the outlook. If anything, it felt like this was a sign from above that this was meant to be. Little did I know that I would get many more signs from above in the next 30 minutes, some of which give me goosebumps still today when I think about them.

I told Dale that I wanted some time alone to go read my letter out loud and burn it, so he stayed back far enough on the trail and took photos, lost in his own world. I got to the overlook, sat down on the ledge and started to read my letter out loud. The tears flowed. I don't even recall all of what the letter said, except how I told him I forgave him for everything and I loved him before signing my name.

As I finished reading the letter out loud, I wanted to take in all of my surroundings and remember the moment, so I took out my cell phone and started recording video. I sat there in silence and cried. As I scanned the sky after crying more, I spotted an eagle in the far distance. I couldn't believe it. Ever since my dad died, whenever I saw an eagle, I thought of him. It's probably because we played "On Eagle's Wings" at his funeral and it's a favorite church song of mine. Dad was circling me, telling me to burn the letter and let it all go. Yet, another sign from above.

I recorded the eagle for a bit and thought about how that was no coincidence (there are no coincidences with God). As my tears began to dry, I decided it was now time to burn the letter. As I mentioned, it was a windy day. I grabbed my phone and started to record on video again. This time I'm not sure why I wanted to record…maybe to capture the memory for later. Getting up from the overlook's ledge, I set the letter down and put the lighter to the paper. It started burning and took just seconds to go up into flames. Just as it was finishing the quick burn, the wind blew away an unburned piece.

Because I didn't want any shrubs or grass to catch on fire (we had burn restrictions for our area because of the dry conditions), I ran after the little scrap of paper that was left. I picked it up and started to cry all over again. The piece that was left was shaped like an eagle's head with the black/brown char mark on the outside of the shape. The words left on the scrap included "self," "cry," "forgive you," and "love." I cannot make this up. This was yet another sign from above that this important step would be the start of even more healing.

A few weeks later after this particular event, I would sit at Sunday Mass and hear Fr. Ron talk about how forgiveness was "for giving," meaning forgiveness was a chance to give a gift to someone. I thought about the gift I'd just given myself with this letter. All the resentment and anger that had been building for years was slowly going up into those flames. I realized there was more "for giving" I would need to do when it came to myself and the actions that led to my rock bottom.

· 3 ·

The Perfect Storm

*"Living a life worth living isn't going to just happen.
You have to be willing to do something different."*
—*Jen Nelson, LPCC*

 **To understand** how to move forward, you sometimes need to know where you were coming from. There were so many revelations of an eating disorder and body shame in my own words right there in my own journals. My authentic voice just wasn't louder than my Ed voice. My journal entry on Sunday, May 22, 2016, reflected that. (Please be aware that these are pre-recovery words, dominated by a diet-centric life, so you will see words such as "food addiction," which is not a thing, by the way, "healthy foods," which it is not helpful to classify foods as good or bad or healthy and unhealthy, and the thought of "if only I had enough willpower."):

> *"I'm so bothered that I can't quite crack the code of why I overeat and sabotage myself. What is it I'm afraid of? I eat a ton of food at dinner and then a big dessert that leaves me feeling stuffed all the way up to my chest. That's how I feel now and I regret it. I ate a quarter of an apple pie and ice cream. Instead of logging it and moving on, I'm still regretting it two hours later. Why don't I want to log my food? I'm afraid of what the story might tell me? How does one figure out what's going on psychologically? What am I afraid of? I'm afraid I won't succeed – and the only person I'm hurting is myself. I only know how to beat myself up – I*

33

wasn't taught how to be kind to myself. I won't have to rely on anyone else if I screw up. Why don't I eat healthy foods? What am I afraid of? I mean I know it all comes down to calories in vs. calories out. Is it that I won't draw attention to myself if I hide behind my weight and big-girl clothes? Part of me is afraid to fail. And afraid to succeed. Will someone expect more from me if I lose weight? Maybe the weight represents a cushion of sorts from all the pain I endure. Maybe if I lose all the weight, Dale will leave me? Maybe if I lose all the weight I won't have anything to work on? I don't know what's gotten into me. I've struggled with losing weight for over 20 years. The battle is over. I'm bound and determined to get to the bottom of my food addiction. Food will no longer control me. I will become my best friend and walk this journey with myself, through the good days and bad. I want to be healthy. Maybe in my subconscious I feel like I am healthy? Maybe I tell myself that I'm going to have a heart attack anyway, so I eat food to comfort me.

I'm taking back my life! Food will not control me. I am healthy and will continue to get healthier each and every day. Perhaps I feel like I should be able to do this on my own and because I'm not, I sabotage myself by eating? I know I'm struggling. Food is my worst enemy. It shouldn't be this hard. It is hard. My weakest link is my food. I must have some psychological attachment to food. Food is comfort. I need to think food is nourishment. How does one stop being addicted to food? How does one separate the psychological attachment to food? What is food giving me? Tonight it was apple pie and ice cream as a reward. I went to the grocery store when Dale was supposed to go. And then guilt happened shortly after I ate it. Still almost three hours later I still feel guilty.

God, walk with me through this food addiction. Thank you for allowing me to see it out in the open. That is a good step in the right direction and toward recovery. I know You'll guide me through this addiction. You'll be there by my side on the days I crave the food – the sugar, the salt, the carbs. I know You'll walk with me. I know this is happening for a reason. I wish I knew why. I know You'll allow it to come to light when the time is right."

Instead of turning to a psychologist or therapist to help with a recovery that was right there in my own journal in my own authentic words, Ed led me to choose another diet plan a day after this journal entry. This would turn out to be my last diet, but the reasons for it being my last were not what a habitual dieter would have expected. It's not that I had finally hit my weight loss "goal," rather it was because I was finally being led to eventual freedom from an eating disorder that had been with me for years, under the radar of everyone, including myself.

The very next day after writing this journal entry, I would call the Weight Loss Clinic associated with my healthcare system. My former general practitioner was now the director of this program. She was the same doctor who told me I had an unhealthy relationship with food just five years prior in 2011. My first appointment would be the following Friday with this same doctor. *I'll fast and have all the blood work done, and then will meet with the doctor to talk about the program. Then, I will have class from 9-10 am. I will also need to take three classes and commit to a monthly weigh-in appointment. Easy peasy*, I thought. *Finally, I will be free*, I thought.

The clinic was not close to home, and yet I was willing to commit to the commute once a month, as I really wanted to get a "grip" on a good food program with support from a "real" doctor and clinic I trust is what I thought at the time:

> *"Weight Watchers is a good program. I just need something over and above that will teach me nutrition and wellness. Many of the concepts will be the same. I'm sure I'll have example menus and need to track. I think for this program it will be specialized and all about nutrition. I hope to learn how to eat healthfully. I was hoping for one-on-one coaching from the doctor too. And to address the psychological issues I have buried."*

I not only chose to start this weight loss clinic program, I also started acupuncture, as I had heard it, too, could help with weight loss. Since 24 sessions per year were covered under our health insurance plan, I started going weekly that spring, about the same time I started the Weight Loss Clinic. I told the acupuncturist that I wanted to lose weight, so she gave me herbal supplements to take and had me boil up chicken with some natural herbs that tasted horrible. It was all in the name of weight loss, at least that is what I thought at the time (now I go to this same acupuncturist for my general well-being. No herbs for weight loss needed).

Meanwhile, my new job of just one year at a new company was becoming even more stressful. Our business partners were very demanding and our own team was turning against one another. Instead of confronting the toxicity directly, I chose to eat comforting food and drink soda and frou-frou drinks, i.e., turtle mochas from the coffee shop. Going to get a Caribou every work day morning became a comfort for me. It took the edge off what I would have to face that day in the office. And it was an added bonus that one of the baristas knew me by name and my drink order, so she would start making my drink the minute she saw me coming from the skyway. I continued this practice well into my recovery journey, but it gradually decreased over time as I confronted all the internal issues and began asserting myself at work. It eventually ceased all together and became a once in a while thing for me.

The Friday morning of my first Weight Loss Clinic appointment, my tummy was rumbling hard and loud; I had to fast for a blood draw. Feeling drained, I really wanted to shed the burdens in my life once and for all and to have control over my body size. Everything else felt out of control. I even journaled how:

> *"I'd be kidding myself and anyone else if I said I'm not nervous about starting this weight-loss program. On my good days, I'm all in, but on my bad days, I struggle and struggle hard. I simply don't want to work at it. My job is stressful enough. I don't want another 'job' to have to work at. Shouldn't it just happen because I'm a good person? I fear this program won't work either. I'll pay a ton of money and the doctor will be tough on me and I'll still weigh what I weigh today at the end of the day.*
>
> *What if I say that the hard work needed was more important than all the effort I put in on my job? What if I started putting myself first – really first over all the shit at work? What if I let everything else go – the expectations, the churn, the chaos, the negativity – and focused on myself? What do I need at this moment? I need kindness, forgiveness, love, attention. I'm the only one who is in*

control of those things. And they all come from within. No one job, number on the scale, words from someone else, pat on the back, etc., will work. From within, I will seek what it is I need. I will search for happiness from within and stop seeking it from everyone/everything else."

I had no idea that all along, my core self knew exactly what I needed and my Ed voice was getting louder and louder each time I journaled these authentic thoughts and words. He kept leading me to weight loss efforts because my own core voice was getting louder and he wanted to stay in charge.

During my first appointment, I was placed on an appetite suppressant. The pill the doctor typically prescribed caused heightened anxiety, so she prescribed an alternate one since I was already diagnosed with generalized anxiety. I was worried when I picked up the prescription from the pharmacy, as it said not to take it if you had high blood pressure or family history of heart disease. I had high blood pressure and my dad died of a heart attack (and had his first one at age 42), I told my doctor this when she called to return my message. She said I wouldn't be on the drug long and that my blood pressure was under control with medication, so I didn't need to worry. "Remember, we need to treat your obesity like your asthma – as a chronic illness," she would say. Reluctantly, I swallowed that first pill. It was another time where Ed won the battle.

The diet plan that I was to follow (along with the appetite suppressant) was to eat between 50-75 net carbs per day, with five or less grams at breakfast, 80 grams or more of protein per day, between 1100-1400 calories per day, and to eliminate processed and sugary foods and white starches like bread, rice, pasta and potatoes. These were "bad" foods on this diet plan. Over the course of the next several months, I would decide that a filet mignon and a side of broccoli for breakfast every morning was the "correct" plan.

Each Sunday, I would ask my husband to grill up the $50 worth of steaks for me for the work week so I could have them for breakfast. He commented one time, "This seems like the Atkins diet to me," to which I responded in anger, accusing him of not supporting me. This would take much undoing during my initial time in eating disorder treatment. I wish I had only realized that it was just like the Atkins' diet myself at the time and that something was off when I went for my first weigh-in after one month of being on the appetite suppressant. I had lost seven pounds in that first month, so they had me hold that amount in a fat mold and took my picture. They congratulated me on how much weight I had lost and how wonderful I was doing at "putting in the work" to make the changes needed. I remember thinking, *what changes? I haven't made any changes. I still eat the same food and am still stressed out.*

On my drive home from my initial appointment, my boss called me. I let him know I was driving home from my appointment and would be home in about 20 minutes. He said he needed to talk to me about something and that I should call him back when I got home. My anxiety went into overdrive on that 20-minute drive. I was so worried I'd done something wrong – something about the contractors we were letting go, my associate's behavior, me not working more than 40 hours in a week, me leaving at 3:00 p.m. on Thursday, me working from home that day, me at this doctor appointment. *It had to be something about me* is what my anxiety and Ed told me.

I would later learn when calling him back that it was *not* about me. It was about the software development manager he was hiring. Only through my therapy during treatment would I learn how to better handle these situations in the future. Thankfully, I'm to the point where if my boss tells me he needs to talk to me now, I don't jump to the conclusion that I have done something wrong.

I've come a long way!

· 4 ·

Hitting Rock Bottom

"All feelings have a purpose."
—Jen Nelson, LPCC

 *I really* have come a long way. Looking back though, I still had further to fall. I was forced to hit my rock bottom before I would reach a trail to freedom. It all started to brew about three years prior (in 2014) to my diagnosis. I (Ed) wasn't happy with my job of ten years, even though I was at a solid company that had given me a lot of opportunities. Living with an Ed (and anxiety), I thought I deserved more – more pay, more responsibility, a bigger title. Never satisfied.

A common thought was, *I've given my employer my life, and what have they given me in return?* Only now do I realize this was another one of Ed's ways of being sneaky. If Ed can fill your head with negative thoughts about how you don't like a job, you won't focus on getting rid of him and your own authentic voice and thoughts remain silent. It will always be someone else with Ed. Someone or something else is always to blame and is the problem. And because Ed is good at "saving" you, he will create scenarios that make it seem like you need to be saved (i.e., a company he tells you is no longer good enough).

The resentment that had been building and brewing for a few years was the same kind of resentment I had with my dad. It was a pattern. Build up the resentment, let it brew, continue to "pick the scab" so to speak, then numb to escape. Because Ed led me to believe it was always someone else – whether my dad, my kids, my husband, my team members, my boss, or whoever – I was lured to believe I needed an easy escape. "The food will help take the edge off," Ed would say.

Sometimes, my escape was soda in large quantities. I recall going to the cafeteria at work in the morning and again before the cafeteria closed around 2:00 p.m. It got easier for me to go whenever I wanted after they installed a check-out register that allowed you to swipe a credit card on your own. They had a fountain soda pop machine that became my go-to "reward" for a tough day…or even the thought of a tough day ahead.

At first, I would fill up a 32 oz cup with diet Mtn Dew because *at least it is zero calories and zero points. There is nothing wrong with that,* and yet I despised the taste of diet soda. Soon, it became 30 oz of diet Mtn Dew mixed with two oz of regular Mtn Dew. Then, 24 oz of diet and eight oz of regular, until eventually it was more like 30 oz of regular and two of diet. It was a quick fix. I became consciously aware of this habit when one of my direct reports said to me, "Hey, I see you have your Big Gulp this morning." My Ed voice saw this as an opportunity to shame me. *Someone caught us. Shame on you for not keeping it our little secret.*

Soda pop became something I had to work on healing my relationship with, taking months of work in sessions with my dietitian during treatment and at home. I would tell my dietitian in a one-on-one session that it was like my Ed voice was a child molester when it came to soda pop. He'd pull up alongside me in a beat-up car as I walked down the street to the bus stop, roll down the window and slyly ask in a deep, Barry White kind of voice, "Hey, kid. Want a ride? I've got some sugary soda in here. It will help take away all your worries and get you there fast."

I couldn't escape his voice. I'd spend months with my dietitian trying to heal all the shame when it came to soda pop. "No foods are bad," she would say. She would go on to say something like, "Your eating disorder is equating soda pop with unhealthy food, so whenever you drink it, you want to mindlessly do it in secret because it negates that you drank it. You go for the diet kind because that is what the previous diets would say makes it okay." It's "okay" because of being zero calories they (the diet plans) would claim.

Also, because my eating disorder had placed soda on a pedestal of shame, it had become a taboo beverage, something you should not have. Of course, when you tell yourself you can't have something, it's only human to want it more. And then when you go so far as to deprive yourself of something you really enjoy, when you do drink it, it's in large quantities, thinking maybe this is the last time I'll ever have it. The whole cycle starts again.

During one of my one-on-one dietitian appointments with Katherine, I brought in a 20 oz bottle of Coke with me, as we agreed to have a working session centered on drinking the pop mindfully. I couldn't even bring myself to take one sip of the thing because of the instant shame of drinking it right there, out in the open, in front of my dietitian. She was so patient and supportive. The tears just rolled down my cheeks. I had no idea how much control soda pop had over me until that moment. All the unintended, yet hurtful, Big Gulp teasing made me feel so ashamed. And yet, it really wasn't about the soda pop. It never was and never would be.

The feeling of shame rising up meant there was something I was avoiding. Something I wanted to escape from. It would bring me back to my childhood when I wanted to escape the pain of being in an alcoholic and codependent home; back to fifth grade track and field day when the boys in my class teased me and called me "Tick Tock Titty" because I was going through early puberty and wasn't wearing proper undergarments. I am still working on my relationship with soda pop and trying to drink it within "loving limits" as my dietitian would say.

Back to my job and the mounting stress in 2014. I was putting in long hours, working a full day in the office, then booting up my laptop at home, living on an overload of caffeine to survive. Often, I arrived at work early (around 6:30 am) for meetings with my team members in our Bangalore, India, office and worked until 10:00 or 10:30 at night. My candle was burning on both ends, just like Dad did. Food and soda were the escape I used from all the stress and unhappiness with my changing body.

One of my mentors suggested that I pick only one day a week to work in the evenings so I could free up my time to do other things I enjoyed. How absurd, I thought. I have to be online, always preparing for tomorrow and never missing an email. My anxiety and eating disorder fed off of each other in these instances.

As it hit home a little more, the toll it was taking on my family life started to sink in. I had already missed out on a lot of my kids' younger years by this time. Toward my remaining months at this company, my daughter asked me one night, "When are you going to get off of that thing" (my laptop), to which I replied, "In a minute," to which she replied, "You always say that." Yikes. Do I really?

I also began realizing the toll this was taking on me personally. Toward the end of my tenure at this company, I started to pull back a bit, vowing to get a better handle on things (back then, this meant going on another diet) when I started at a new company. I dug my heels into deciding that I needed to go all-in at Weight Watchers. Since 2011, I had been paying my monthly subscription, but the scale was only going up. This would be it. I'd get serious this time. I'll leave this company and devote my time to my diet and losing weight and become a whole new me. I'll do whatever it takes to lose the weight "for good." This will lead me to freedom, I thought. At the time, I had no idea I would be led on a different path toward freedom, one that would bring lasting freedom and recovery.

In early 2015, I was offered two competitive job offers, both at very good Fortune 500 companies based here in Minnesota. One would allow me to maintain my current title of "manager" and the other would not. I didn't know it until four years later in therapy, that my identity had become one with my title. If I had a fancy title, it meant I had made it in life. Dad would be so proud of me for how far I've come, I would think. Eight years after his death, I was still seeking my dad's approval when I took the manager job!

At the time, I didn't see the pattern that I have since become aware of (after a few years focused on my recovery). When the going got tough, I would much rather escape than confront reality. You need to keep harmony at all costs is what my Eating Disorder voice would tell me. My employer was what I desperately needed an escape from at the time, or so I thought. In hindsight, I realize it was only an escape from all the assertive conversations I needed to have to set healthy boundaries.

I showed up at my new job, committed to "starting over" with my approach to work and life. I was going to dig in to losing weight for good, and then I would accept my body. At the time, my life revolved around whether I lost weight or not. Each Thursday, I left the office at 3:00 p.m. so I could attend my Weight Watcher meeting in Inver Grove Heights. I felt like this was good for my own self-care. My striving nature, however, made it extremely uncomfortable to leave the office when people who got there before me in the morning were still there when I left. Because I had such low self-esteem due to my eating disorder, I would numb these feelings of conflict and guilt later that evening.

Self-care at that time meant only one thing: losing weight. After all, if I could only lose the weight, everything else would come naturally. I'd be more confident. I'd be more assertive. I'd be happy with my job. I'd find a better job. I'd be more…you name it. Losing weight was the key to my happiness and success was the lie my eating disorder fed me every single day. Louder and louder, it would say, "Your body is disgusting. If you lose weight, people will respect you more. Who can respect someone your size?"

When Weight Watchers was no longer helping me keep off weight I had lost, I would turn to the clinical weight loss program mentioned in the previous chapter. This is it. This will be my last diet. I will lose the weight for good and I will instantly love myself and have ultimate confidence. The weight is in the way. These were all the eating disorder thoughts buzzing in my head all day long.

I seemed to have "success" on that weight loss clinic diet…or did I? Really, it was all because I was taking a drug that prevented me from feeling my own hunger cues! I would later learn, in programming at The Emily Program, how much all these pills and years of dieting impacted my ability to even feel my own body's hunger and fullness cues. We have these cues when we are babies and young kids, yet they fade, ever so slightly, with the first diet you try, until they eventually become obsolete after multiple diet attempts. A diet is literally like starving yourself, because you are restricting calories.

My eating disorder made me think I felt so good at the time. After just four months on the drug, I had dropped to my lowest weight since 1997 when I was on my first ever Weight Watcher diet. At that time, I only wish I would have known that the weight I was at (before any diet pill or diet plan) was within my own body's set point weight range. It wasn't until eating disorder treatment programming when I would learn this. Because my weight as an adult placed me in a higher BMI category, I instantly assumed it meant I was not good enough and had to lose weight.

Even though I was losing weight and felt good about the number on my scale, I was crumbling emotionally and mentally. On the outside, my appearance was changing, but on the inside, everything was the same. I still avoided conflict. I still had unhealthy boundaries. I still hated the size of my body. I still placed blame on others. I still sought approval from others, especially my boss and husband. I still used food for comfort.

At one of my weight loss clinic weigh-ins, I remember mentioning I had eaten a Pop Tart for breakfast when she asked. After the doctor went off on me about how a Pop Tart had no nutritional value whatsoever (it wasn't the five net carbs I was supposed to eat for breakfast), I felt so ashamed. Once home, I binged on as much food and soda as I could stomach. I'd disappointed her. I let her down. One year later, I'd learn that all foods fit, and that a Pop Tart actually does have some nutritional value (thank you Emily Program for allowing me to see that)!

My inner world was continuing to unravel. The summer before my son started high school (September 2016), he started hanging out with kids we didn't know. These were the kids he was going to play football with in the fall. He decided to play football again after taking a break from it for four years after suffering a concussion in the fifth grade during practice. *Where was his best friend these days* I wondered. My husband and I worried about drugs, yet he promised us he was not doing any (and we would later learn this was the truth, even with all the temptations around him).

He went through girlfriend after girlfriend the fall of his freshman year. One time, he was dating someone, and we didn't even know he was dating. Another girl he would break up with on Halloween and become friends again near the end of that calendar year. He was sleeping a lot over winter break. His best friend was never coming around. His grades were slipping. He would have angry outbursts. We thought it was drugs, yet he kept assuring us that he was not doing any.

Then the day came that shocked my world. Just after Christmas break, I was in the high school parking lot, waiting to pick up my son for an appointment with an allergist for his constant sinus infections. I was just about to text my friend Shari to complain about the shitty day I was having at work and about my boss when my cell phone rang. It looked like a school phone number so I answered.

"Mrs. Schmitz? This is the school psychologist at Park High School. We know you are here to pick up your son for an appointment, but he's here in my office with me. Did you know that your son was planning to commit suicide?"

The rest of what she said in that moment was blurred, as I was still trying to comprehend "suicide."

When I finally comprehended what she was saying, I asked a question. She responded, "Yes, I know. Ian said you would be surprised, and that he wants you to know he feels very loved at home and that this would be hard on you," the psychologist said. "He's had a falling out with his best friend last year. Did you know about it?" she continued.

I didn't. I felt like the world's worst mom. Here I had been thinking my son was doing drugs, when this whole time the signs were there for depression. I'd been so busy worrying about my own problems, which included losing weight at all costs, that I failed to see what was right in front of me.

We got Ian the help he needed with a local family therapist. He was diagnosed with depression and anxiety and attended weekly therapy for a while. I am forever thankful for that ex-girlfriend who told a teacher that Ian had told her he wanted to commit suicide. Even though they are no longer dating, nor friends, she will always be someone I remember as bringing attention to my son's attempt at suicide.

My work world was beginning to unravel at about this same time. The project team I was on when I first joined this company in 2015 was becoming super toxic. It had been toxic with our business partners since day one, yet now our own IT team members were against each other. We'd gone through three different software development managers in the first 18 months I was there.

I will never forget the camel that broke my back. I won't go into detail, as it doesn't matter, yet I knew it was time to move on to another team within the company. I could not take the toxicity any more.

My boss said they valued me as a team member and that I could talk to two of his peers to see if they had any positions for me. I talked to one director, but her projects sounded just as stressful. The other director had an individual contributor role for me on her team. I hemmed and hawed about her position. I could keep my salary, yet I would no longer be a manager. My boss at the time told me it would hurt my career. The other Director told me she wasn't waiting forever for me to make a decision. The next day, I accepted her individual contributor position.

Just as I was finding out about my son's suicide plans, I was moving into an individual contributor role. I hadn't been in this type of role for over nine years. My whole identity had been ripped from me. At the time, I quickly regretted my decision to switch positions, yet it was a quick-fix decision that was so natural (like a go-to decision on autopilot) whenever the going got tough. *Remove yourself from the conflict, as quickly as possible* were the ever-constant thoughts when conflict arose. In my eating disorder treatment programming, I finally learned that sometimes the best thing for your own mental health is to sit in the muck, radically accept what is at the moment, and continue to work toward your long-term goals. "This, too, shall pass," is often what I would hear in programming and therapy.

To add to this storm, the doctor at the weight loss clinic mentioned that I was gaining weight as she was weaning me from the appetite suppressant. "My son just tried to commit suicide," I said. *Cut me some slack*, I thought in my head, yet didn't feel comfortable saying out loud (remember, avoid conflict at all costs). It's like she was on the same side as my eating disorder, shaming me as much as Ed did. It was about this time that she told me I had an unhealthy relationship with food. *No duh. You told me that six years ago in 2011 as my GP, and I checked that off the box when I went to the therapist you sent me to.*

I ate through all the rough feelings, whether those were the hurtful words at the weight loss clinic or at work, or the need to assert myself and being unable to do so. I finally started seeing another therapist (Mari) in March

2017. I felt like I was making progress, yet the same themes were coming up over and over when it came to anxiety, food, my body, conflict, and shame as noted in my journal on May 2, 2017:

"I had my annual gynecology visit today. Dr XXX was called away to deliver a baby right when I got there so I had to see the nurse practitioner instead. The nurse took me back and weighed me. It said XXX – a full eight pounds up from December and another 2.3 pounds from my doctor appointment visit on April 7. Yikes! I feel like a failure. Like I let myself down. Like I can't get that one piece of my life in control. This is the one area of your life you <u>refuse</u> to address. You go get put on meds to lose weight, starve yourself, go full-throttle until you reach XXX pounds, all the while "tricking" the body with the food you were eating. It didn't catch up with you until now. This has been out of control since October. I remember telling Karen (my friend) that I ate like crap for a month, yet lost weight in October. How? I didn't care at the time because I met the goal of losing weight. I didn't learn the process. I didn't change underlying behaviors. No. Just keep checking stuff off a checklist and kid yourself and the doctors. The weight comes off, yet your habits aren't healthy.

The going is getting tough again right now, so I want to give up. And part of me does. Part of me feels like a failure and part of me says I don't care. I'm my own worst enemy. I want to have a healthy relationship with food more than anything. I don't want to hide food. I don't want to stuff myself beyond belief and then feel miserable. Why is this so hard? Why do I hurt myself with food? What is it that I think food is giving me that I'm not giving myself in healthier ways?

...I know it's not a quick fix, so why did I seek out Dr XXX? It's no different than Weight Watchers. I can lose weight, but I lose weight to lose weight and check it off my list of stuff to do. Healthy eating habits don't stick for me. I'm good for a period of time – three months maybe, then a few bad habits start coming back, and then a few more and a few more again. Next thing I know, I'm eating the same crappy food as before."

I drew some pictures below this journal entry that simply break my heart today. I had absolutely no empathy for myself in these dark moments and thought the only way to happiness was weight loss. I absolutely hated my body and everything about it. My eating disorder had full control over these words and the pictures. One picture I drew was of a broken heart with "divorced from reality" written next to it. I drew the number from the doctor's office scale and made little flashing lights around it saying "Glaring statement." I drew a paper with the grade of "F" written in bold at the top of it like you would get in school. Next to the "F" I wrote the word "Failure." A sad face was added with the word "Disappointment" next to it. I drew some bricks and wrote "ton of bricks" next to it and a door that said, "No one will know…" And finally, I drew a nut that was cracked and said, "The one nut I cannot crack (figure out)."

So much pain lived in those pictures and words, yet I thought it was me. *It's all me. I don't have the willpower to lose weight and make it stick. I don't try hard enough. What is wrong with me?* Like I said, I have so much empathy for myself now. This journal entry completely breaks my heart today.

About two months after this journal entry, I would continue the slide toward my complete breakdown. It was early July by then, and what happened one night was a sign; I was not taking care of my own needs. To this day, I am still not sure if it really was vertigo like the ER doctor suspected or if it was simply a panic attack. Either way, my body was giving me early warning signs. The alarm bells were firing, but I wasn't listening.

On the way into work that morning, there was a road sign in our neighborhood that I had never seen before. Road construction was underway on the main neighborhood street that led to the highway, so I was forced to take the detour. It was a foggy morning. Suddenly, the sign that read "Blind Hill Ahead" appeared to me as I waited to make a left turn. I had never seen it before, even though that was the familiar road I often drove to pick up my kids at their elementary school.

Later that evening, I journaled about how that sign must have been a sign from above. I thought it meant I was going to take a new direction at work. All the possibilities got me excited, and I noted my ideas in my journal that night. Little did I know that the stress of my life was actually causing me the blind hill.

Just as I finished journaling about the possibilities, my son stopped by my room to say hi. As I looked at him, I started feeling lightheaded and dizzy, and said, "I'm not feeling so well." He mumbled something about hoping I felt better soon. Thinking a bath might help, I could barely look myself in the eye in the bathroom mirror. My world was spinning. Something felt off. I called for Dale to come up to the bathroom. Luckily he was home from work; he had worked a double shift the day before.

My heart felt like it was going to give out, and my world was still spinning. The top of my head hurt. Dale helped me take my blood pressure, which was only slightly elevated compared to my normal. I laid down on the bed. I got cold. Then hot. Then, burning sensations went up my back and to my shoulders.

I attempted to get up to go into the bathroom again. I could barely walk. My arms got heavy...really heavy. My world spun faster. Laying down on the floor, I told Dale to call 911. They arrived shortly and assessed that I needed to go by ambulance to the ER. Just as I got into the ambulance, I threw up. I asked for water as they put in an IV in my arm, but they didn't have any. Then, I threw up again on the way to the hospital. They told me to hang on to the puke bag and not to drop it on the way (not the nicest EMTs that night).

After the second time of throwing up, I started to feel a little better. At the ER, they drew blood and took a CT scan. Something showed up on my scan, so they wanted to do an MRI. All was okay with the MRI though, so the doctor thought with the dizziness and headache that it was vertigo and sent me home with some meds. Years removed from the situation, I think it may have been a panic attack, yet it was another sign of the "blind hill" ahead.

In late summer, about a month and a half after that incident, an even bigger whammy happened. It was the last straw of my already fragile mental (and physical) state. My oldest child, Kaitlyn, headed off to Mankato to attend the university there. My whole identity was rocked. I fell into a deep depression, crying constantly at the thought of her being gone and also at the thought of her having her whole world in front of her. I was stuck in this middle-aged body, had a trail of bad decisions to look back on and was stuck in a job I hated (at the time). Kaitlyn had her whole world ahead of her, and I only had regrets. This is something I kept telling her over and over, none of which was appropriate.

Life felt like it was unraveling at this point. Food became an even bigger escape. I remember going two miles out of my way on the way to work to stop at a local gas station. I'd get a 32 oz regular Mtn Dew on the way into work. This was after eating breakfast at home, and then breaking off half the tube of Pillsbury cookie dough to take on the run to numb the pain. I'd sip the entire 32 ounces on the short 12-mile commute to the office; I didn't dare bring the Big Gulp around in public anymore.

Then, I'd get into the office and numb with Caribou. I'd get the tea with zero calories on the days I'd stopped for Mtn Dew, and the other days it would be a turtle mocha. The warm drink would taste so good and coat my stomach; the stomach that I would later shame when looking in the mirror before getting into the bathtub. I'd cover it up with a washcloth when reclining in the tub so I couldn't see it. I was ashamed. *How could I have let myself go?*

All of this kept adding up to the point where Mari told me I needed to go get some help, as she didn't specialize in eating disorders. I'm so glad she did. My last appointment with her was on Halloween morning, the week before I started The Emily Program. I let her know I was starting with them the next week. Once in programming, I wrote her a heart-felt thank you note, thanking her for all her help. She mailed me a note back saying she was so happy to hear I was making progress at The Emily Program.

Starting My Journey: The First Week

"What other people think of me is none of my business."
—Jen Nelson, LPCC

 **After** my initial diagnosis in late October 2017, I would hear from Lindsay, the Office Manager at the Woodbury location of The Emily Program. It was the following Monday, and I ventured from the open cubicle farm at the office to a small conference room on the first floor of our building to take her call. "I guess I will do it. Why not now?" I told Lindsay on our first phone call together. She told me the Intensive Outpatient Programming (IOP) started the following Monday, November 6, at 5:00 p.m. She let me know what to expect. "You will meet with your dietitian, Abbie, for orientation, and then your therapist, Miranda, before programming, so plan to arrive by 3:00 p.m." She also scheduled 30-minute weekly dietitian appointments and one-hour weekly therapy appointments for the next several weeks. "How long will I need IOP?" I asked Lindsay. "Everyone is different, but most are in programming for four to 12 weeks," she replied.

I thought this was going to be a straight shot. *Four to twelve weeks isn't that bad. Such a small period of time. I'll cure my "disease" and lose a little weight* I thought. It was just another thing to "check off" my already full list of to-dos. But I had no idea how far from the truth all of this was; it was such a blessing in disguise! Because I thought The Emily Program would help me lose weight for good, I really was part excited and yet part apprehensive to start. What still remains truthful among all those initial thoughts was that

I would unravel a lot of layers. That is exactly what happened, one step at a time. For this, I am very thankful.

The next set of business was telling my boss about my diagnosis and that I would need to leave early some days when my appointments were before programming. In hindsight, this is not something I would recommend. You do NOT have to give your diagnosis to your boss. Usually, I left the office by 4:00 p.m., but now would need to leave by 3:00 p.m., depending on the appointment, the day of the week and the weather. We were approaching the long, brutal winter season in Minnesota, when road conditions can be awful and unpredictable.

In hindsight, after many hours of programming and finding my courage and strength, I would realize that telling my boss all of this was not necessary. She did not need to know my diagnosis, and later regretted telling her. I was a salaried employee who was not paid by the hour, rather by the results. Sometimes bosses don't see it this way, and she was one of them.

I had a one-on-one meeting with my boss the very next day – Tuesday. It was unusual, as most weeks she would reach out to cancel or say she was too busy to meet. This week, I would tell her I had to share some news, so she kept the time as scheduled. Here is a snapshot of the agony in my journal the night before that meeting with her:

> "I've got a long journey ahead of me, but it's what is needed to start recovering and healing. I'm going to miss a bit of work, and I'm going to have some long days. It's what I need though. I'm worried about bringing this up to my boss. I don't want to appear weak or uncommitted (to work). There will be two days a week I have to leave early. Otherwise, I'll leave at my usual time, unless the roads are bad. As far as my boss goes, I may tell her about next Monday and Tuesday's appointments, but maybe nothing more. I don't want sympathy or extra oversight. I just want to feel okay coming and going as I need to."

There was continuation of agony the next morning, the day I would tell my boss, as noted in my journal that morning:

"Shame. I feel it right now. Tears. They roll down my face as I try hard to stuff my feelings. I don't want this disorder. I don't want to tell my boss, because she will think differently of me. I don't want to be punished or judged. I already do that enough myself. But God, do I ever want to recover. This is the only way. To dig deep into the disorder and take it head on. You will not win, Mr. Disorder. I will come out ahead this last time. You've controlled me too long. I deserve happiness. I deserve joy. And it's all going to come from within.

Thank you, Lord, for bringing me to the awareness of my disorder. I appreciate the gift You've given me. Thank you.

Tears are dried. I feel better letting it out. And not continuing to eat as I rolled through the feelings (I am eating breakfast). I just named the feelings and it felt freeing. I look forward to continuing to name the feelings on my way to recover."

My boss lived in a different state than me, so we used video conferencing for meetings. I used my video like usual for this one-on-one; she did not. I was huddled in the same small conference room as the previous day when talking to Lindsay about the programming details, trying to be as quiet as I could so no one who sat outside would hear me.

There was a lot of small talk at the beginning – the *how was the weather* kind of talk. This was often what I nervously did when needing to have a tough conversation with someone. I don't exactly remember how I transitioned to tell her, but it started out a little bumpy. I started to cry and the words just struggled to come out of my mouth. "Just tell me," she would say directly, in an almost demanding way. "It can't be that bad," she continued to say. Then the words just vomited out of me. "I have been diagnosed with binge eating disorder and will need to be in programming four nights a week right after work. I'm going to continue to work and manage my care."

Her response sticks with me to this day. "I know. I have a hard time with my weight too. If I were you, I'd continue to work and manage too. Good choice. Make sure you send me an out of office memo so if Ann (her boss who is in my same location) is ever looking for you, I know where you are."

She would have no idea the impact of these words on me. It was like she was diminishing my pain and diagnosis because I was so wrapped up in getting her approval. It's not until much, much later in my recovery when I would realize none of that was about her, rather the fact that I wanted her to validate my own feelings for me.

I desperately wanted her to tell me what I needed to hear at that moment, because my own core voice was buried deep and was not brave enough to come forward to validate my own feelings. My core self was brave enough to tell a work friend what I wanted to hear a short time later. "Why couldn't her words have been, 'I can see how hard this is on you right now. I can hear the pain in your voice. Why don't you take the rest of the day off. Please let me know how I can support you going forward.'" Even that work friend had no idea how to offer support. I had just verbally vomited on her too, again looking for someone else to validate my feelings and be my own voice that was buried.

Quite honestly, mental health and the office don't mix well in today's society. It's taboo. "Don't ask. Don't tell," is the mantra, yet mental health is extremely important. We don't turn off our emotions at work. We are whole beings. We don't leave half of ourselves at home…the half of us struggling with mental health for the day. People at work are unprepared for these kinds of conversations, and we cannot expect them to fully understand (I believe this has changed slightly since I was first diagnosed).

After this, I decided to not ask and not tell at work, so when a peer of mine asked why I was upset over something else our boss had said in a meeting, I shut down. It's only after she kept persisting that I spilled the beans. Her response was not what I expected. "I suffered from an eating disorder (anorexia) when I was in high school," she would say. She shared a few more details with me. I felt so "normal" at that moment, right there in that executive's office we were sitting in for the impromptu conversation. It felt freeing in a way. I'd have someone to go to in the future when I was struggling at work.

At this time, I would tell only one other person at work: my former boss who had just taken on a new role on the project I had vacated a year earlier. I was struggling with my current boss about her response to an issue one day, so I turned to this former boss for advice. When I broke down crying, she probed me about why I was crying, so I told her.

When we gathered for a colleague's retirement lunch just one month into my treatment, I would regret telling this former boss. I wasn't very far into my recovery, so I struggled eating in front of anyone who knew my diagnosis. *She knows, so I have to eat healthy in front of her.* I ordered a sandwich I wouldn't normally get at this favorite downtown St. Paul restaurant of mine. It seemed like a "healthier" option compared to the fried egg sandwich I wanted to get.

Being so new into my recovery journey, I felt like my former boss was watching me eat like a hawk. She would later tell me how she felt sorry for me having to eat while in the company of others. I don't think she understood the depths of an eating disorder and was really only trying to help. At the time though, I just didn't see it this way, so I binged on popcorn right after getting back from that lunch.

I was still in the position to always please my boss, even former bosses, and it felt like I had let her down in so many ways. My dietitian would later recommend that I schedule lunch with her again and eat my entire plate without worrying what I was eating (or if she was judging me). About three months into my journey (about two months after this incident), I did just that.

Going into my first day of appointments and programming at The Emily Program on November 6 was nerve racking. *Who will the others be?* Lindsay said something about the other clients having a similar diagnosis, but she did not (and could not) tell me any details about them. *Were they my age? Were they my size?* I wondered in the days leading up to that day. The weekend before my first day in programming, I journaled extensively, and all sorts of ups and downs and thoughts about the possibilities came together all at once:

> *"I'm a bit scared of my upcoming journey toward recovery. What if I don't recover? What if I only continue to gain weight? This makes it scary. I don't want to fail. I don't want to live in shame about what's in my cart at the grocery store or what size my clothes are or*

what's on my plate at lunch when at work. I want to eat without shame. I want to recover from all the bruises on the inside, deep within my soul. I feel ready.

What if I <u>do</u> recover? What will that look like? It would mean I love myself exactly as I am in the moment. It means I fuel my body with food that nourishes me. It means I look at myself in the mirror and say, 'I love you' every single day and night. It means I praise God for all my body has to offer. It means food no longer controls me. It means there is no more shaming. It means I accept setbacks as small bumps in the road and talk healthily to myself to get back up. It means I get back up. It means I fall down and get back up. It means I just breathe. It means I thank the Lord for my body. It means I am living my life in the ring, rather than on the sidelines as a spectator. It means I love myself like no tomorrow. It means I praise myself for all the progress I've made. It means I ask for help and see that as healthy and okay. It means I'm moving forward and not looking back.

Thank you, Lord, for giving me this wonderful opportunity. I feel so blessed by You. You keep moving me closer to a healthy lifestyle, which isn't just about nutrition. It's how I treat myself and how I let others treat me. I want to love myself completely as You would want me to. I want to use my talents in the best way possible."

And then the day came…the first day of programming. I worked a full day and packed both my lunch and dinner before leaving for work in the morning. We would need to bring our dinner and a dessert each night, except Tuesdays. Tuesdays were the nights when we would cook together or we would go out to eat as a group. I liked those nights. This would be my morning journal entry before starting programming later that same day:

"Well, this is it. The day I start my recovery process. I'm ready, yet I'm nervous and afraid. Will I recover? Will I put in the time and commitment needed to succeed at recovery?

I really do want to heal. I deserve it. The Lord has given me this chance for a reason. I don't want to blow it. I want to appreciate

*it with all my heart. I'm just afraid of the commitment of time –
from 5:00-8:00 p.m. four work days. That's a big commitment,
but it's a gift. How many opportunities will you get like this in
life? Not many and the good Lord brought me to this gift, so He'll
get me through it. Let me put all my trust in Him. He knows the
plan and I just need to trust in Him on this one. He led me here
for a reason. Let me not question why or what will happen. Let
me appreciate the gift. It is a beautiful one."*

I agonized over what to bring to eat for dinner that first night. Lindsay did
not say *what* to bring – no guidance whatsoever. I was going to eat in front
of others, so my eating disorder told me *we'd better be good* and pack a small
portion of whatever we brought. We could binge when we got home or in
the car before the appointments. And honestly, at that time I thought The
Emily Program was going to be like a diet program; they will tell me what
to eat and I will log it somewhere.

When I arrived to the Woodbury location, I was frazzled having come from
work. Work stressed me out. My boss stressed me out. My colleagues stressed
me out. The parking ramp stressed me out. Getting out of downtown on
time stressed me out. I was a bundle of stress, all tightly wound in a ball,
walking mindlessly throughout the day.

I sat down in one of the chairs after checking in with Lindsay at the front
desk. She welcomed me and told me to have a seat. There were tables of
puzzles here too, just like at the Como location. Too nervous to let my guard
down, I sat in silence until Abbie called me back.

Abbie was incredibly nice. She would only be my dietitian for the first three
months of my treatment; she got transferred to help with day programming
at the Como location. She let me cry and was really patient at that first
appointment. She explained how the process worked with IOP, but I don't
remember many of the details. I do remember thinking *She is not like any
other dietitian I have met. She's kind. She 'gets' it. She wants the best for me.*

Next, I would see Miranda, my therapist who was eight months pregnant. I
was reserved and didn't share much with her that first night, yet I would cry
with her too. I wasn't sure what to expect and was anxious to see who would

be in IOP with me. Would I know any of them? Because I was under the impression that eating disorder treatment was going to be yet another diet plan (ugh, I know, right?), I even asked Miranda, "What if I fail at this?" By fail, I meant what if I don't lose the weight like I thought will be prescribed? She reassured me there was no way to fail, yet it would take me a while to fully believe this was not a program about losing weight and that dieting would become a distant memory.

I went back out to the waiting area after my time with Miranda, waiting to start group programming. There were three other women out there waiting too. I assumed they were in my programming with me. They all seemed about my age or a little older. I was relieved. Knowing I wanted to remember this special moment for a lifetime, I captured the following thoughts in my journal about eight minutes before programming was to start:

> *"I'm here. At The Emily Program. I just finished my intake session with my dietitian, Abbie, and then my therapist, Miranda. I have to admit, I'm a little skeptical. Did I make the right decision? Will I succeed as I want to succeed? What's going to happen? I'm scared. My shoulders feel heavy and my right upper arm is sore. This is a BIG commitment. Am I committed? I want to run. I want to hide. I want to have an easy button. I don't want all this work…*
>
> *Yet, I'm ready. I want to heal. I want to recover. God gave me this gift for a reason. Let me take it all in and not overthink any of this. Let me take things as they come and stay completely present in the current moment. NOW."*

Abbie and Miranda took us back to the group room. We walked single file down the hallway back to the room, no one saying anything. The room was warm and inviting. It was filled with several comfy living room type chairs and two couches. We each found a spot that felt comfortable to us in the room. Later, we realized the spot we had on the first night would become "our spot," and as the group grew with more clients, we would become slightly territorial with these original spots.

I chose one of the armchairs. It was leather, comfy. It kept me guarded from the others in the room with the armrests on the sides. A nice coffee table sat

next to it to put my water bottle on. That table also he
and fidget things to use if you wanted. Across the rooi
good friend, Stefania (who, of course, I didn't know on th
became my good friend and a beacon of hope during my

Another woman, Bonnie, who was probably in her late 50's or early 60's, sat to the left of me in another one of the leather armchairs. She was very guarded that first day. At the end of the night when Miranda said we could exchange phone numbers with each other to text each other when needed, she didn't want to share her number. Bonnie would eventually open up with us and share her number, but would soon drop out of the program during the Christmas holiday. She was gaining weight and still employed with Weight Watchers, who had a strict rule on how much she could weigh she told us. We lost contact with her as we continued on with our journeys, yet I always prayed for her to find peace and another job so she could finally recover from her eating disorder for good. She just wasn't ready at that time.

Another woman, Brenda, in her late 50's, sat on the leather couch to my right. Brenda would eventually lay down on the couch as her back was in pain from a car accident a few weeks prior. All of us struggled with binge eating disorder, and she also suffered from bulimia. She had just been released from a 30-day residential treatment, where she was living in a group house. I would offer prayers for her too, as she would be released from programming at the end of the year when her insurance company no longer covered her to be in IOP. I also learned that Brenda was diagnosed with breast cancer a month later. She continues to be in my prayers today. I don't know where she ended up with everything since we lost contact about a year after she left programming.

We each went around the room and said our name, what brought us there and our spirit animal. Then, Miranda and Justine (another therapist helping that night) handed us a binder full of info on Cognitive Behavioral Therapy (CBT) concepts. We would need to bring this binder each night. Justine reviewed the schedule for Tuesday dinners. We would be making dinner the next night and go out to eat the following week. There was a Friends and Family Night at the end of the month when we would bring in family members or friends to join us for dinner. All other nights, we were responsible for dinner ourselves. They encouraged us to bring food

ᴜre in the cupboards and refrigerator for the week so we didn't have to
ᴜmember to pack a meal each morning before work.

About one hour into our evening programming in the comfy room that
first night, we were excused to go to the bathroom before our dinner hour.
Miranda told us we needed to have at least two of us in the bathroom at all
times. This was to prevent anyone from purging in the bathroom, especially
after dinner. That note on the toilet from the Como location now made
sense. If you didn't have someone with you in the bathroom, you were more
likely to purge. No flushing the toilet if you went to the bathroom alone.
Since this location's bathroom was shared with other businesses, that note
was not on any of the toilets we used.

I dreaded that first dinner hour where I would have to eat in front of others.
And this would be different: it would be a full hour, and we would process
our emotions before the meal, during the meal and after the meal. A lot of
emotional stuff in that one hour! At home, I would usually take only five
minutes to eat my dinner. And I was proud to be part of the clean plate
club, so when they told us we had to eat everything on our plate during
programming, this was not hard for me. What was hard for me was pacing
my meal and processing my feelings at the same time.

My meal was leftovers – some homemade beef stroganoff I'd made in the
crockpot the night before. Fretting over what to bring, I packed a small
portion and skipped bringing the homemade "Becky bun" that was always
a side dish with this meal at home. My husband named these buns "Becky
buns" several years prior, and the name stuck (and still does to this day).

Since I needed to show them I knew how to eat right, I didn't want to bring
too many carbs. After all, the stroganoff was on top of noodles (another
carb). It had to be the right portion size, the right amount of carbs. *This is
a diet program* I had thought when packing my dinner, but I would have
this myth dispelled this very first night of programming. Thank goodness!
For my dessert, I brought two pieces of mini chocolate squares. Again, I
didn't want to look like I didn't know how to eat the correct portion size.
I was blown away when Abbie told me that five mini pieces (yes, five) was
the correct serving size for our programming rules at that first dinner hour!

I cried eating those chocolates. "What is coming up for you, Teresa?" Abbie asked. "I'm fat and don't deserve to have dessert. Dessert isn't for fat people," I would respond through tears. The only one to cry at the dinner table that night, I was partially embarrassed and partially relieved. I was being authentic on that first night and wasn't holding anything back. Tears would happen for the others on their own terms. And there would be a lot more tears for me in the coming weeks!

We processed our emotions after the dinner, went to the bathroom and ended up in the comfy room for another one hour. We worked on identifying an IOP goal for the week. Mine was to prolong a binge episode by 15 minutes. It was a lot to take in. We were excused to go home a little before 8:00 that first night.

About 15 minutes after arriving home for the day (after leaving the house at 7:00 a.m. that morning), I was exhausted, and yet would capture the following thoughts in my journal:

> *"Just got home from my first night at The Emily Program. I survived. I am not alone. I feel on the right path. Words of wisdom from Justine (one of the therapists): 'You are in the car. You have control over the eating disorder. You are driving forward. You are in the driver's seat. You started by walking through those doors. There is no perfection; only PROGRESS!'*
>
> *I survived my first day. Yay! I know I can recover. I will recover. It's gonna be tough, but there is no losing. There is only winning or learning.*
>
> *I'm surrounded by all the clearance Halloween candy I bought at Cub on Saturday. I want the candy as a reward for finishing my first night, but that's the eating disorder's voice. That is not mine. I will wait 15 minutes to see if it passes. I have a headache too. Overwhelmed and need a good night's sleep instead. I will take care of my real need: sleep and rest."*

The next morning at 7:00 a.m., I captured the following in my journal:

> *"Here I am. Parked in the Victory Parking ramp on Wabasha Street in downtown St. Paul. I don't want to go into work today, but putting one foot in front of the other is the only way toward freedom. The heat from the vent in my car feels good. Just a few more minutes, Lord. Don't take away this sense of peace I feel. Even though I don't want to go into the office, I know God is on my side and is cheering me on to take the steps to go into the office.*
>
> *Maybe this journey will lead me to leave this place to somewhere my skills are capitalized on. Maybe. Maybe I will leave this place and be cut from the chains I feel. Day in. Day out. Same old shit. I no longer want to live like this. Recovery. Let my recovery lead me to where it is I will thrive."*

Before entering programming for night number two, I would capture my thoughts again. My journal became my easy go-to during my journey. I was grateful journaling came natural to me. It was like spilling my soul right there on paper, a point in time to be remembered when the details would long escape me:

> *"My tummy hurts. My left shoulder feels burdened too. But I am back for day two of programming. I just checked in for my initial dietitian one-on-one appointment and found out I am going to pay over $200/wk for this treatment. That's a big chunk to pay, but it's needed. I really do want to recover. I want to confront my disorder and heal.*
>
> *I had one tough episode to conquer today. I had eaten lunch and had a dull headache. I was craving Mtn Dew, so I told myself I had to wait 15 minutes to let the eating disorder lose control. In the end, I went and got the Mtn Dew after about 25 minutes of battling with myself in my head. I'll call it a small victory as I wanted to start delaying my binge by 15 minutes this week as a goal. I still caved into the craving, but at least I waited 25 minutes. It was a conscious decision, and I drank it without guilt and only half of the 20 oz bottle. All small victories.*

I really miss my husband and my connection with him. I can't tell
if it's just heightened because I'm not seeing him, or it's always been
there and it's calling loudly to me."

That night it happened again...the tears, that is. We would make spaghetti, meatballs and garlic cheesy bread as a group. We also made a chocolate mousse for dessert. Looking back on this night two and half years later, I think this was intentional, since most of us thought carbs were "bad." That's what the diets tell you. It's what my weight loss clinic had been filling in my head with for the past year.

As a side note, I was completely weaned from my appetite suppressant at the end of the first month of IOP, as you cannot cut those pills out cold turkey without adverse consequences. Back to the spaghetti. We made two types of noodles, one type of meatball, as well as some plain ground beef, two different pasta sauces from a jar and a recipe for some cheesy bread. Abbie forgot to buy the salad for our meal, so we would count the sauce as our veggie that night. "It's all about flexibility," she would say.

It was fun cooking up our pasta meal together. We were joined by Abbie, Miranda and Julie, another therapist. When it came to dishing up our plates, no one wanted to do it after Abbie dished up her plate first to show us. She took a healthy portion of noodles, a couple meatballs and some ground beef, sauce, and not one, but two whole slices of cheesy bread. "I can't eat that much," I said. "I'm fat. And you're skinny. A fat person like me can't take that much, and you can because you're skinny. Plus, that's too many carbs in one meal." Then, the tears started.

After she thanked me for being honest and authentic, she challenged me to think differently. She said not to compare and to eat what felt satisfying to me. She reassured me that what she served up on her plate was acceptable for me to take onto my own plate, regardless of size. We needed to eat what our bodies needed. Sometimes we may be hungrier than other times, and we needed to listen to our hunger and fullness cues. I didn't know mine though, and it's something I am still working on today. It can take years to get back these cues that were so natural to us before we started restricting on our first diet.

We had so much distraction (talk and conversation) at the table that night that I actually ate just enough to feel satisfied. I left a little pasta on my plate and about half of my dessert. That felt like an accomplishment to me. It (the food) did not control me during that meal.

When we processed in the comfy room with Julie, I said how I was worried about tomorrow's meal already since I "shouldn't bring in fast food." Julie would challenge me and say that a sandwich and chips from Jimmy John's is fine to bring in. If it's what we want and would be satisfied with it, it's okay. Abbie soon joined us after cleaning up the kitchen and agreed. There is no right or wrong food. Still having a diet mentality, this was hard for me to accept. *Isn't there supposed to be a prescriptive menu and I can only eat what's on that menu? That's not reality anymore, and I'll need to work through this.*

I would process in my journal, my go-to, shortly after arriving home from this night of programming, a portion of which was this:

> *"Even though my shoulders feel like a ton of bricks on them right now, I feel at peace. Life is going in the direction I've needed it to for years. It feels good to be getting the help I need. I want nothing more than to be healthy in my relationship with food and blossom into the flower my name signifies (my mom always told me that Teresa means "Little Flower"). I deserve happiness. I deserve joy. I will recover from my eating disorder and continue to move forward in the other areas of my life. Life is too short to be unhappy. First things first. Let me heal and recover from my Binge Eating Disorder first."*

The next day, Wednesday, was an emotional one for me in the office. That seemed to be a theme for me at this time in my life. I had a lot of anger built up about my boss and what felt like her lack of support for me. Rather than have an assertive conversation with her or radically accept it like it was, I would hold it inside, slowly eating me from the inside out. Remember, it was always someone else. Feeling emotionally exhausted after work that day, it had taken a lot of my energy to show up to work.

What stands out for me is the group support I was starting to feel from my fellow recovery warriors on this journey toward recovery. *They get it. For the first time in my life, I feel like I am "normal." These women have the same thoughts going on as me. They dream about food. They spend their day figuring out when the next binge session would happen to relieve the pressure cooker.*

The next day, Thursday, would be another repeat. I would journal these thoughts just 33 minutes before IOP on Thursday:

"A tough day in the office. Not enough to do and me paranoid about my calendar being open for my boss and others who walked by – almost felt like Dan & Pricilla (two of my peers who also reported to my boss) were asked to watch over my every move. I feel powerless. I feel stuck. I make too much money and can't find something else...I don't feel supported, so I feel shame for everything and like somehow I deserve this shitty feeling. I even have heartburn right now – top of my chest. I was super hungry throughout the day and just wanted to eat. I didn't, but the urge is super high right now. If I wasn't coming here to The Emily Program, I'd be in trouble. I'd go home and have a pity party. I'm stressed. I don't want to feel this way and feel like it's me who just needs to adjust my attitude and be grateful for the job, yet I feel underutilized, and that's a shame."

Even though I had a shitty Thursday work day, I would quickly come to learn through programming that everything comes and goes. Nothing is permanent. "This too shall pass," took on a whole new meaning for me and the others. It took some time to realize this, yet it proved to be true. By the close of our programming on that same day, here is how my emotional state had shifted in less than four hours:

"I am feeling good. I made it through my Jimmy John's dinner, with chips and two Butterfinger fun size candy bars, and almost all of my sandwich. I don't feel stuffed. I don't feel deprived. I feel satisfied. I feel successful. And I had Jimmy John's!! Earlier today, I was hungry. Really hungry. And I felt ashamed. Tonight, I feel much better. I'm not hungry, and it's been almost two hours since I finished eating.

I am so thankful for The Emily Program. It is helping save my life. I will get to a good place mentally and emotionally. I will do what's right for me, even if it's not right for others. I am taking care of myself, and it feels so good right now. Thank you, Lord. Thank you for this gift."

The last working day (Friday) of that first work week during IOP, I would do something I rarely ever did in my past. In fact, I don't recall ever doing it before this day. In my past, I would just push through it and continue, until resentment turned to anger. My health always lost out to wanting to be seen as responsible. My mom once told me the story of when I was in elementary school and never wanted to stay home sick. She would tell my teachers how she wanted to "tie my leg to the piano bench" on the days I was sick so I couldn't walk to school. Yet on this day, for the first time, I was taking back my life and tuning in to what I needed most. I called in sick. And I didn't feel one bit of guilt. I needed good mental health, and it was one of those days.

I made a surprise trip to see Kaitlyn in Mankato that day. It was just what my soul needed. It fed me in more ways than any Mtn Dew ever could.

· 6 ·

Letting It All Go

"Keeping anger, even just a little, invites resentment.
Keeping guilt invites shame."
—Jen Nelson, LPCC

 **November** turned into a month of great progress. I continued to muddle through my work days, one day at a time, and my three-hour IOP programming four nights a week, along with weekly dietitian and therapy appointments. I was managing it all with great stride. Bonnie, Brenda, Stefania and I were all texting each other around the clock. We were there for each other. We understood each other. Sometimes it was an inspirational quote, and other times it was a lifeline, looking for a life vest because we'd fallen out of the boat.

Continuously examining my work environment, I was trying so hard to fit in, to be someone else, just so I could stay at the company. At the time, it felt like I was "hustling," as Brené Brown calls it, for my own self-worth. Look at me. I can do all these things for you. You need me. It's only much later in my recovery journey, I mean much, much later, when I would find peace and comfort that there was no hustling needed. It's all part of the journey through. You need to go through these moments and really feel them and experience them to make any progress.

Speaking of Brené Brown, I spent time reading her book, *The Gifts of Imperfection,* (I am a big fan of Brené) one weekend early in my programming.

After reading, I drew a picture of what life is like with recovery. Then, I would write my own "When Everything Feels Good in My Life" story as Brené talked about in her book[3]:

> *"When Everything Feels Good in My Life . . . I've meditated in the morning. I've journaled. I've connected with Dale. I've had a relaxing weekend. I've walked. I've taken care of my own needs. I've gotten a good night's sleep. I've done something I enjoy. I've prayed and gotten close in conversation with the good Lord. I've spent time outdoors in the sun. I've rested. I've used my creative juices. I've spent time with my family. I've learned. I've read."*

None of my "When Everything Feels Good in My Life" had anything to do with food, body size, or weight, yet those were exactly the things I had spent years chasing. *If I lose weight, I can feel good. If my body was smaller, I'd fit in regular clothes and I'd get the promotion I "deserve." If I lost weight, Dale would want to be with me intimately on a more frequent basis.* The list went on and on. The more I chased, the more I loathed myself. It was a vicious cycle, especially having an eating disorder driving the bus.

In IOP, we spent time making picture collages of what recovery looks like. I still have my picture today. I cried making that, as did Brenda. We wanted recovery so bad, we could taste it right then and there. *Would recovery taste as good as the Mtn Dew?* That same night, we learned about the "ABC" method of exploring your thought process. A is for the Activating Event, B is for your Beliefs and C is for Consequences. An Activating Event is an actual event or situation, a thought, mental picture, or physical trigger. Beliefs are what you were thinking as it happened, things like what thoughts were going through my head? What is my most distressing thought? How much do you believe the thought? Consequences are the words to describe how you feel – the words that you most feel.

One afternoon, I decided to try this process while waiting for programming to start, when reflecting on a situation at work with my boss. My thoughts were always buzzing about work and how unhappy I was. Radical acceptance with my current work situation would not come until about two and a half

---

[3]   Brown, Brené, 2022. *The Gifts of Imperfection*. 2nd ed. Hazelden Publishing; Anniversary edition.

years into my recovery during a worldwide pandemic, but more on that later. With this situation, my boss had me working with Visio – a software program for creating diagrams and infographics.

A: This Visio diagramming was a task I didn't really want to do to begin with.

B: I was getting frustrated with all the software applications that were not included on the original Visio diagram I was working with, so I started to draw a new picture. Then, I started to talk about being a perfectionist, so I went back to the original picture and tried to update it again. The thoughts of being a perfectionist came back.

C: I ate a whole snack pack of Club Crackers. I felt under-utilized. I was feeling angry at having to do the stupid exercise. *I don't have enough to do. They don't realize my potential. I deserve to be happy.*

Now that I am far removed from this situation, I can see what was really happening; it had nothing to do with my boss, the assignment, or my place of employment. I had always proven my worth by being super busy, to the point of exhaustion, when living fully with my eating disorder. It meant I got a 4.0 in school, an A+ on the test, the latest promotion, the latest accolade, the latest whatever. I equated my whole being with this measuring stick. Boredom wasn't something I had experienced before. If a person was bored, I thought it was a sign they were lazy.

Crazy busy was what I always felt. I wore it like a badge of honor. If I was crazy busy, it meant I didn't have time to tell people how I really felt, nor even think about how I really felt. I didn't know how to function if bored. My best friend Heather, who didn't know of my diagnosis at the time, once asked me, "What if it was always supposed to be this way (feeling bored) and you've been overworking all this time?"

Later, I would come to accept these feelings. It didn't mean I was unworthy. I didn't need to hustle anymore. How freeing that would be.

The second Tuesday of programming, our group headed to a local Mexican restaurant for dinner. The four of us ladies made the short commute to the restaurant in Brenda's car after we spent the first 30 minutes processing in the comfy room. There were four of us clients, two dietitians and two therapists. It was a one-to-one ratio, which was unusual. This time we had a new dietitian, Katherine, who was training under Abbie, and an additional therapist along too.

Abbie ordered chips and guacamole for the table, and then suggested that I order two cheese enchiladas to get enough protein. I would order only one, that also came with a side of rice and beans. I still didn't want people to think I ate too much, even though my own dietitian was recommending two enchiladas. I always had an aversion to guacamole before that night, even though I had never tried it before. *It won't taste good* is what my eating disorder would tell me. A picky eater since early childhood, I've thankfully made progress since then. But I remember my mom running through other options she could make if I didn't like what she had made for dinner, as if she was both the chef and the short order cook all in one. "Would you like a grilled cheese sandwich? A bologna sandwich? Hot dog?" etc., silently exhausted, until I would agree on something or officially declare, "There is nothing to eat!"

In this instance at the Mexican restaurant, I discovered I liked guacamole after all, yet not before I caught myself looking for approval to take the chips and guacamole. I looked at Katherine's plate to see if she'd eaten all her food, especially since she had ordered two cheese enchiladas. Comparing my plate to another's and needing to "stay on my own placemat" was something I would work hard on throughout my journey. Sometimes I still struggle with this today, but I have made tremendous progress.

After our meal, we ordered fried ice cream. All eight of us shared two portions. I felt like we deserved it. Much later in my recovery, I realized feeling like *I deserve this* was most likely my eating disorder talking. When we processed our feelings after dinner, I said that I felt like I ate too much. I said that I was full from my meal, but felt I deserved the dessert.

Abbie and Stacy (a substitute therapist) challenged me to remember that some days my body may be hungrier than others and this is okay. "Just trust your hunger cues," they would say. I told them how I was upset because I wanted this program to be a prescription of things to do and boxes to check, and then it all magically works, yet it wasn't working that way. As we continued to process after dinner, I acknowledged how freeing it felt to say I was full and to reveal my feelings about deserving the dessert. In its own way, it was comforting to hear that I wasn't alone. Bonnie, Brenda and Stefania agreed that they wanted the dessert too.

The next morning, I would look for approval on something from my boss yet again. Later that day, I journaled about how I was tired of "hustling" for my worth when she didn't give me approval. That instance caused me to think *I want to leave my company*, the all-too-familiar escape option (almost like the seatbelt I wore every time I got into the car and never realized it was there while driving). But I would tell myself something wise in my journal: even if I got a new job, "I'm afraid I will hustle no matter where I go because there is not enough love and worthiness (inside)." This was the first time I would challenge myself about running. Small, yet big, progress for sure.

The ups and downs of an eating disorder would continue to happen even though I made this small, yet big, win. I would go binge on Laffy Taffy from a container at work because my boss told me I needed to accept a new project that was being given to me from her boss. "It will hurt your career if you don't (take on the project)," was her directive. I felt like my life was being constantly controlled by others and I had no voice to speak up for myself.

While waiting in my car to go into programming later that same day, I binged again. Then, I journaled the following:

> "*I am stuffed. I ate a lot of food in five minutes flat. In my car. While outside in The Emily Program's parking lot. I feel shame for eating it all and worthy for having it at the same time. My boss and I don't see eye to eye. She is so cold. So distant. I can't wait to move on from her.*"

The running (escaping) was so familiar. It was my go-to. *If the going gets tough, you need an instant escape.* Feeling any uncomfortable feelings was to be avoided at all costs, let alone have a conversation with my boss to set healthy boundaries. I can see the patterns now, yet could not see them at the time. It was always my boss, my employer, my kids, my husband, whomever. It was never me and never my eating disorder.

On Thursday, I decided to bring in Culver's for dinner at IOP. I brought a kid's meal: cheeseburger, small French fries and a scoop of frozen custard with pieces of Reese Peanut Butter Cups on top. I'd drink the small root beer that came with the meal while driving to IOP. It was my eating disorder's way of preventing anyone from judging me. A big meltdown happened at programming that night. Abbie and Miranda were talking about dessert and how we may not get it some nights. Remembering the fried ice cream at the Mexican restaurant, I thought that comment was aimed toward me, so I felt super ashamed having brought it in with my Culver's meal. On top of that was a tremendous amount of shame for drinking the root beer on the drive there.

When we sat down for dinner, I started to cry. "I can't go into the kitchen and eat," I said. Abbie and Miranda pulled me aside and asked what was wrong. I didn't want to tell them. I let them down by what I brought to eat, plus I drank the soda on the drive there. They gently waited for me to stop sobbing. Through tears, I told them they hurt my feelings by what they said about dessert and how I was already ashamed about the soda and what I brought for dinner. Although I was brave to tell them, I couldn't look them in the eye. I had let them down. In my journal later, I encouraged myself, saying maybe I couldn't look them in the eye that time, but eventually I *will* be able to. I added that someday I will do the same thing when I'm at work and in other relationships and situations.

By the end of two weeks in programming, I would note the progress I had made in my journal:

> *"I believe God granted me my recovery gift because I needed it. It was time. It was what I needed at this moment in time. It's hard living with an eating disorder, but it's hard not addressing it too. Today is a new day. I will go about loving myself and taking care of myself. It's what I need. God wants me to heal <u>inside</u>. He wants me to get healthier on the inside.*
>
> *I know my eating disorder wants me to hang onto it for the rest of my life. It wants me to fail at recovery, because then it can make*

it feel like it's in control and I'm out of control. It wants that more than anything. I want recovery more than anything. And for the most part, I am moving toward recovering. Like everyone says at The Emily Program, recovery looks like a twisted old fashion phone cord, and we want it to look like a straight line. And that's okay. There are some days when it feels like I've taken ten steps back, and other days I feel in total control. The eating disorder rears its head when I try on pants that I could fit into two months ago. It shames me for gaining weight back. I fight hard to calm its roaring voice. I try to say I love myself <u>AND</u> mean it. Part of you wants to throw in the towel and just say that you give up, and yet a part of you says you got this."

During the third week of IOP programming, I would start to realize how challenging it was living with an eating disorder. Exhausted physically, mentally and emotionally, it felt like I did not have much to offer any one person, except myself. I had to be reminded often to put on my own oxygen mask first before assisting another passenger on the plane. So simple, yet so hard to put into practice. During my first month of programming, I was talking with Miranda, my therapist, about how I had a full-time job, was still a mom, wife, sister, aunt and friend, on top of my commitment to the IOP program. In hindsight, I wish I would have taken a leave of absence during the first two months of my intensive programming, but my eating disorder was pushing me to "do it all."

I would capture the following emotional toll in my journal the morning of my third Tuesday in programming:

"One step at a time is right. One foot in front of the other. Literally. Having an eating disorder is hard. You'd almost rather have it be cancer or something that's more "accepted" and people rally around. Having an eating disorder feels shameful; like it was my choice, whereas with cancer, the "victim" is never blamed. Help comes out in so many ways. People rally around cancer. They shy away from an eating disorder. Yet people with an eating disorder need as much love and support as a cancer victim.

In some ways, having an eating disorder feels like a prison. You are trying hard to recover and carry on with life at the same time. You want to heal, yet you are ashamed to tell anyone, let alone ask for help. "I just need to get my life in order when it comes to food" is what goes on inside your head and in other people's. Society isn't nice. Eating disorders aren't nice either!

My therapist, Miranda, tells me that I could explain it like cancer; you need the eating disorder treatment to keep you alive. You wouldn't just do one chemo treatment if the doctor told you five were necessary. You have to fight the eating disorder as much as you'd fight cancer – with all your body, strength, mind and soul. With an eating disorder, we are fighting a relationship with food and our body. Society tells us we should eat a certain way and look a certain way, so it's hard to fight an eating disorder. And it's not about the food. It's not just saying, "Then don't eat x, y or z," or, "Go on x, y, z diet and lose weight." It's just not that way.

I don't know when I'll recover, but I know without a doubt it's what I need right now."

On that same Tuesday, our programming hosted a "Friends and Family" session, which meant you could invite your friends and family to dinner. I wasn't ready to have my husband mix with this group yet, and I had yet to tell any of my friends about my diagnosis. What would my husband think about the group? And I was really nervous about what he might say. He is outspoken and speaks his mind. What if he says something to offend someone in the program? I'd have to face these same people the next day, and I wasn't ready to be vulnerable yet.

Brenda had her two adult sons come, and one brought his wife. Bonnie brought her husband. The love I saw between Bonnie and her husband made me experience a pang of envy. He was so supportive. They shared loving glances at each other. He joined into the conversation so well and told the story of how they met and their first date at a Twins game. Brenda's sons and daughter-in-law talked about their support for their mother and the arrangements for the upcoming Thanksgiving holiday. She was surrounded by love. I felt alone in this instance – even though it was my decision to not ask any family or friends to come support me.

Recovery and living with an eating disorder is hard and real, even when you are making progress. The Wednesday before Thanksgiving, I had my weekly dietitian appointment with Abbie. Each week, our meeting began with being weighed. She would face the weight display away from you so you could not see the number, and she would not tell you the weight either. For some reason, I happened to see the weight display that day. It said a number my eating disorder wanted to shame.

I would journal later how the number made me feel big and troubled me. It made me feel fat and that I needed to go on a diet. Eventually, I would learn during treatment that fat is not an actual feeling, yet I had been saying that is how I felt for years! I didn't want to weigh what the scale said; what I really wanted was to weigh what I did at my lowest in the Weight Loss Clinic the year before. The number from a year ago felt good. The Eating Disorder voice said, "You've gained so much weight."

When Abbie told me I had maintained my weight over the past two weeks, I didn't believe her. Thoughts ran wild. *I bet I gained weight and she just doesn't want to tell me. She doesn't know I saw the number.* So sneaky Ed was. He would continue a few days later and tell me, "Since the number is up so much from a year ago, you might as well just say f*ck it and go to town on popcorn, soda and candy at the movies. You deserve it and shouldn't give a damn." And then it shifted gears to shame again. "It's no wonder where you are at considering all the food and soda you have been drinking."

My first Thanksgiving in programming was during week three, and I would have a successful day. As usual, I woke up to my alarm clock and journaled for a bit in the quietness of the morning. It was so quiet, I could hear my five-month-old puppy named Ollie snoring softly near me. In that moment, a realization hit: *life is good.* This puppy could snap you out of your worst day by bringing you two stuffed toys and nudging you for attention, all the while joyfully wagging his tail.

Not long before this moment, I was adamantly against getting him. We'd not had a pet since we put Patches, our first (and only) cat, down to sleep when Dale was in Iraq with his Army Reserve unit 14 years prior. There were plenty of good reasons not to get him. Ollie was only ten weeks old. Kaitlyn would be soon heading off to college. I was in a tough spot emotionally, as mentioned in my previous chapter. But Dale and the kids really convinced me.

In this Thanksgiving morning moment, I would realize how good it was to have Ollie. He offered unconditional love non-stop, all day, every day. It was like he knew when you needed an extra dose of it. And he was teaching the biggest lesson I needed to learn: offering unconditional love to yourself.

A few hours after journaling that morning, I realized I was a little tired. This time, I would listen to my body. My body said it was tired and needed a little nap, so I laid down. Before eating disorder treatment, my eating disorder voice would bash me for needing a nap after having just woken up three hours prior. And yet on this day, there was no bashing. It felt good to just lie in bed and take care of myself, even if it was only for 15 minutes.

Thanksgiving dinner was at my house with my sister, Missy, her husband and their two adult kids, as well as my mom. It was a nice celebration. After dinner, we played cards and had lots of laughs. It was comforting to know that I was surrounded by those I loved the most on my favorite holiday. And more importantly, this was the first Thanksgiving that I was not beyond full and being shamed by the Ed voice.

As another week of programming was about to begin, I would journal where I was at with things on Sunday night:

> *"We numb our feelings with the food so we don't express how we feel. Then, when we go through therapy and the recovery process and learn to eat when hungry, we realize we have some uncomfortable feelings to let out. We want to turn to food, as that's all we've known for years. If we do, it becomes a meltdown since we are trying to fight the battle.*
>
> *I've walked around in a fog for 25 years. I've not known how to sit with my feelings, "good" or "bad." I feel empty. I feel numb. I feel like I've walked through a haze of life for 25 years, just going through the motions to get through another day. Yet I want to live. I want to feel my feelings. I want to tell people how I really feel and what I really need. I know this is going to mean that I*

upset some people and they may choose to walk away, but I'm only keeping myself in the prison longer by holding back. Pleasing others has put me in a prison for over 25 years. I don't want to be in a prison any longer. I want to really LOVE myself and go to bed at night knowing I did what was best for my recovery. I want to enjoy food and not use it to soothe the pain.

I may not have had the conversation with my boss go as I had wished this past week when I gave her an update on my treatment program, yet I know I will get better at having these conversations because I will be having a lot of practice. I want to ask and state what it is I feel and need. I want to leave any sense of apology out of the conversation. I will not be sorry for how I feel or what it is I need. If I don't let others know how I feel or what I need, how can I expect them to know and provide me what I need or apologize for treating me the way they did?

I want to stop walking on eggshells. I want to stop stuffing my feelings. I matter. I have a voice. I want to feel good when I wake up in the morning. I want to live my life. I want to go to bed at night knowing I did the best I could and I had the conversation I needed to have and said what it is that needed to be said. Why should I go on living a life that hurts at the expense of not letting my words come out as needed? At the expense of pleasing everyone else? What would happen if I stayed in the moment and said the things that needed to be said?"

After the Thanksgiving holiday weekend, our IOP group would expand on Monday with a new member, Kathryn, who would also become one of my good friends. She was much like the rest of us – binge eating, middle-aged and wanting to overcome her disorder. I liked her and how direct she was during situations where I'd be too shy to say anything. There were a few things we shared in common, and one of them happened to be soda pop.

In our group that same night, we would talk about how our eating disorder had become a coping strategy for us or a life preserver for us at some point. It was needed at that time for whatever reason, yet now, it was no longer working. Time to say good riddance to it. Avoiding the work is the eating disorder getting its way. Ed says, "If you don't do the work, you won't ever fail. Stay with me. It's easier this way."

In bed later that night, I would have a much needed and overdue conversation with my husband about how it feels to have an eating disorder. I'm not sure what allowed me to find the courage deep inside to talk to him about how it felt. Maybe it was being in the dark and feeling less vulnerable with the lights out. I was keeping a lot from him, mostly because I didn't want to be vulnerable with him.

He didn't know I ate in secret. He didn't know how much I bashed myself. He didn't know how much the eating disorder was ruling my every move. To be fair, I don't think anyone can ever know how it feels unless you've walked a day in the person's shoes. In all honesty, I was afraid he would reject me if I shared anything with him. I felt the need to keep as much to myself as possible. It's not until much later in recovery (about two years later) when I would finally start to be really vulnerable with him on an almost daily basis. It would take a lot of courage and a lot of therapy to get as vulnerable as I am now.

There was something about him that made me never want to disappoint him and to walk on eggshells at all costs. I had gained weight since we first met. My eating disorder constantly told me I had let myself go and *why would Dale love me this way?* As strange as it may seem, because Dale was a male and an "authority" figure in some imagined way, I wanted to make sure that things were "perfect" so he wouldn't ever abandon me emotionally as my father had.

· 7 ·

It's Not About the Cake...and Never Was

"Thoughts are not necessarily facts."
—Jen Nelson, LPCC

 **I want** to believe things are the way they are for a reason. Deep down inside, I know that to be true. The messiness is required. It's God's way of preparing you for tomorrow. He has everything happen the way it does for a reason. It's no coincidence that I was on Weight Watchers and the Weight Loss Program at my health clinic. That led me to where I am today. It also means all the struggles of today – the pants not fitting, me feeling fat (which, as I mentioned in the previous chapter, I would learn in programming that *fat* is not a feeling) – are all part of a future that looks brighter than today. God is preparing me for something bigger.

Heading into the last month of that year (2017), I had mixed feelings. Professionally, I was still thinking I needed to leave my employer because of my boss, but personally, my eating disorder recovery was progressing. My job was still a large part of my identity at this point, so anytime I struggled with something or someone at work, the urge to move on hit. *I need to take my talents elsewhere. I'll just move to another job.* My good friend Stefania would remind me that I would still encounter the same things at the next job, and it was not about the job.

The same would be true about cake. Katherine, one of the dietitians, suggested that I bring in cake as my dessert to normalize it since it was a binge food for me. After Kaitlyn's high school graduation party earlier that summer, we had about half of a full-sized sheet cake left over; we froze it in our chest freezer in the lower level of our home. I probably ate half of the cake within a few days. Eating in secret, I'd hide downstairs in the utility room. And I would stuff myself until I could eat not a single more crumb.

I did the same for my birthday in mid-November. We'd gone out to eat for my birthday, and the waitress brought me an ice cream sundae dessert. Of course, I ate it, even though I was full from the steak dinner, along with knowing we had a cake waiting for us at home to celebrate with my mom and sister. When we got home, I stuffed myself with cake too, even though I was still beyond full.

Cake was like a forbidden food. It was not point friendly on Weight Watchers and definitely not "nutritionally sound" for the Weight Loss Clinic doctors. Because of this, it had a lot of power over me. If you eat it mindlessly, it won't count, and if it does, you'll just shame yourself into telling yourself you could never eat another piece of cake again.

After Katherine's suggestion, I decided to bring in a small cake from my local grocery store's bakery. It was a marble cake with buttercream frosting, the kind with huge frosting flowers that could make your teeth hurt if you weren't careful and ate too many. I portioned it off with Katherine and kept it there for the week, having it every night for my dessert to begin to normalize eating it in public. It was one-eighth of a sheet cake. Katherine told me to cut it in thirds, and then halves. "That's how I would have cut it at home," I told her, surprised she said to cut it that big.

About this same time in programming, Miranda and Abbie recommended that I start journaling while eating during programming to capture my feelings and thoughts, which could be processed after the meal. Here is what I noted during my dinner at IOP that night:

> *"First bite. I'm feeling okay with what's on my plate: half egg noodles that I brought, plus all the meat and mushrooms, the Becky bun, and about one-fourth cup of corn. We have a new member (Addie), and I don't want to open up with her here since she is new. Half of my hotdish is gone and half of my bun. Only*

ten minutes into the dinner time.

I just checked in about five minutes ago (check in is where we each have to say what is coming up for us and what we are feeling at the time). I still feel like Katherine is being too nice to me about allowing me to eat all of what I have on my plate. And that when she portions, it is typically what I would portion. The same is true for the cake. She allowed me to slice the cake into big portions. I still think she is being too nice to me. She doesn't want me to melt down.

I moved on to my cake. It's 6:35 pm. That's 25 minutes since I started eating dinner. Pretty good pace (I was working on pacing during meals, as I could eat a meal in five minutes or less)."

Just as I journaled these thoughts, I lost it. I stared down at the cake and started crying. "I didn't think I deserve this because I am fat, and Katherine only let me cut it into big pieces like that because she feels bad for me," I said. I went on to say I didn't think I deserved the cake because it's what got me fat to begin with.

Miranda and Katherine said they appreciated my honesty, then started to challenge me (aka Ed). It's not the cake that got me "fat" they said. "The eating disorder did, and you're using cake as a scapegoat." Saying cake made me fat so I can't eat it instead of addressing the eating disorder head-on, challenging him, keeps Ed in charge.

After eating the cake completely, I would continue in my journal:

"I feel full now. Cake is gone in less than five minutes. It's just cake though. I feel really full…like stuffed…like I can't take in any more food. This feels uncomfortable. I've not felt this during programming time ever, so it must be from eating that cake in five minutes or less."

While processing with the group and Katherine at the end of this meal (we did check ins at the end of meals too), I shared how I felt like she was being too nice by allowing me to have that much cake. "That is the correct portion for our programming needs," she assured me. Because my eating disorder voice was still coming up, making it a taboo food, I doubted my own dietitian who had years of training!

Later, Katherine would make Bonnie eat a piece of my cake for dessert too, since Bonnie didn't bring dessert that night or a previous night that week (her days were becoming numbered by this time). Katherine had allowed her to go without dessert one night, but when it became a repeat the next night, she asked if I would share my cake. Bonnie would process that the cake was good and tasted delicious, but it was too much, and now she was going to gain even more weight because of me. I felt terrible. Here I was trying to overcome the control the cake had on me, and Bonnie didn't want any part of it. She was now coming face to face with her own issues.

After our meal and processing time, we talked about how symptom use (binge eating or restricting food) might be out of habit in response to feeling bored or lonely (or any other strong emotions). I felt like a lot of my eating was based on habit. "It's always done this way," Ed would say. We also discussed *sitting with an emotion*…about how it is sometimes more important to sit with an emotion than to fix it. This is something I am still working on to this day.

Later at home that night, I journaled some more about my experience with the cake:

> "…I no longer want to live like this. I want to have cake when I want to have cake and not have a meltdown. I want cake to have no power over me. I want Ed to shut the "F" up. I want him to stop planting seeds in my brain – to make me chase after other "things" so I don't spend my energy curing him and divorcing myself from him. Ed makes me chase after 50 things on the weekends. It's Ed who wants me to move on to other things so he can stay in control when they don't turn out. He wants me to constantly be busy so I don't have time to think about dumping him. He wants to be in control, and he's no longer going to be. I'm in the driver seat. I'm in charge now, Ed! You will not get the best of me. I love myself just as I am, and I can have cake. How does that make you feel, Ed? Does that irritate you? Make you want to stomp your

feet? Well, too bad. You will not take over my life anymore. I am divorcing you and that's final!"

The next night, our group went to a local favorite restaurant, Key's Café, for dinner. We never knew beforehand where we were headed. They would tell us the intention of the meal/restaurant as we started programming for the night, and we would process our feelings before heading there. On several different occasions leading up to this night, I had mentioned to both Abbie and Miranda that I didn't think we should eat breakfast for dinner. They would challenge me and ask if that was the eating disorder or not. I didn't think it was right to eat dinner for breakfast. Later in my recovery journey, I would learn that I actually love eating leftovers for breakfast; it is totally acceptable. Ed really did set a lot of rules for me around food.

On this night, Katherine said the intention for our Key's Café meal was to order and eat our dessert first. "Wait, what? Grandma always said we would spoil our dinner if we had cookies beforehand," I protested during our pre-meal processing. "That sounds like a food rule," Katherine replied. She would go on to tell us that she had heard the restaurant serves large portions, so we could only eat half of the dessert we ordered. *Say what again?*

We finished processing, and then Stefania drove Kathryn, Brenda and I in her car to Key's. Bonnie wanted to drive herself there separately, and Addie was not there that night. We arrived at the restaurant and were seated at a large table with chairs on one side and a booth on the other. I sat on the end of the booth next to Kathryn, and it was time to order our dessert. Katherine let the waitress know that we planned to order and eat dessert first, and then would order our meals. The waitress seemed a little surprised by this, yet rolled with it.

We all ordered a piece of pie with ice cream. I ordered pecan pie and asked her to warm it up. Once the pie came out, and Katherine saw how large it really was, she would tell us to only eat half of the piece of pie and a third of the scoop of ice cream. My eating disorder thought this was a rip off...and a waste of money. When dining out while in programming at The Emily Program, we did not pay for our meals and were not allowed to take any leftovers home. This was the hardest thing to do – to leave food, *good* food, on a plate.

My eating disorder was trying to tell me that I would never get a piece of pie like this again. I believed him, so I wanted to eat the whole thing, as fast as I could. This "never enough" was a common theme for me in my recovery. If I used my "wise mind" and challenged the eating disorder's all-or-nothing thought process, of course I would know I could have this same food again. Key's was only about ten miles from my home, and we went there often as a family.

After having our waitress think it was odd that we all left pie and ice cream on our plates and refused take-home boxes, she was ready to take our dinner order. Since I really enjoyed the farmer's omelet when we came to Key's for breakfast, I'd challenge my eating disorder food rules some more and have breakfast for dinner. It turned out that everyone else ordered breakfast too! It wasn't exactly my first choice for dinner (I would note in my journal that night), and yet it wasn't bad.

I survived this challenge. I ate breakfast for dinner and only ate half of the omelet (they are big too). This seemed to be a big night for me toward my recovery. So many small, yet big, wins wrapped up in that single instance.

And just like in life, there are ups and downs when in recovery from an eating disorder. Dinner at Key's was a win, but the next day would not be. In contrast to the night before, at our holiday luncheon at work, I would stuff myself to the point of physical discomfort. Our leaders said some things I didn't like, so the food became an instant comfort. While sitting with a work friend in the conference room, I grabbed the 20 oz bottle of Pepsi and piled my plate with cheesy potatoes, chicken, a roll with butter and a huge ginger cookie. If anything, the cookie was like the pie and ice cream the night before – a size not meant for one person to eat in one sitting. I would walk away feeling so uncomfortable and so ashamed, as I had eaten beyond physical hunger.

I was so ashamed; when it came time to eat my snack later that afternoon, I felt guilty. Ed told me I had stuffed myself only hours before, and that a snack was not necessary. *I'm going to eat the snack anyway*, as I had committed to eating at regular intervals so I could regulate myself according to what my dietitian had been recommending. During this portion of programming, our dietitians required us to eat three meals a day, three snacks a day and a dessert every day. This was hard, yet necessary. We were "normalizing" food.

Ed tries to convince you that you need to restrict after bingeing or compulsively overeating. He tells you that you should be ashamed for bingeing or overeating, so you hold back on eating (i.e., restrict) your next meal or snack. I remember once saying to Abbie that I don't restrict food. She questioned that, and I told her that was not my kind of problem. "If I restricted myself, I would not weigh what I do." She would challenge me, and she was right. There were times I did restrict myself, and this was one instance where I almost had. While I had a win over the *restriction desire* of my eating disorder, I did not win over the *mindless desire* in this instance. At the end of this snack, I realized I had eaten it mindlessly. I ate it mindlessly so that no value could be placed on the snack itself. This was yet another Ed tactic used to achieve the same outcome: shame.

The next morning, the anguish of an eating disorder would continue. I decided to work from home and head to the doctor for my right arm. In the morning, I was waking up to it being numb, like pins and needles sticking in my hand. It would take a good 30 minutes to stop the tingling feeling in my hand and for the numbing to stop. As I would write in my journal, I would have to stop after a bit from the tingling in my arm and my hand going numb.

That morning, I decided to make pancakes. To anyone else, it was just pancakes, circular discs about 3-5 inches wide and made from a box. Just add water and fry them up on a hot griddle, flipping once. To me, they were so much more; they were the comfort for this morning's pain. I ate three pancakes, trying to be mindful while eating. In my journal, I noted how I really wanted to keep eating all the pancakes I'd made that morning. There was a high desire to binge. I journaled while eating:

> *"I need the comfort; comfort from the pain of my tingling fingers, my arm, and the emotional pain/drain. I want to curl up in a ball and not have to work at all. I have too much angst. I want the pancakes to take away all the pain. I want the pancakes to tell me what to do with my job. Anyone…tell me what to do, yet I know what needs to be done. Miranda highlighted something at dinner last night after I checked in. She said she noticed me say*

*that I portioned something exactly like the dietitians would, and
yet I keep saying I can't be eating all the food or don't deserve it
all. That's how it feels. Like I don't deserve it. Like I'm fat and I
should not be allowed to eat that much. That I should be restricted
because I need to lose weight."*

My eating disorder continued to have me believe that I didn't like my job or
employer so I would stay attached at the hip with him (Ed). It was evident
in the continuation of my journal entry this same time:

*"My plate still has three bites of pancake on it. I feel obligated to
leave something because they were big pancakes. Yet I really want
them. I've not eaten my two clementine oranges or bacon yet. I
just threw out the three bites of pancake. As I washed the plate, I
almost regretted throwing them out. I wanted them, yet I didn't
want to overeat. But really, three bites? I feel like I should have
stopped after eating just two of the three pancakes since they were
big.*

*Okay, it's 7:17 a.m. already. I don't want to even open my laptop.
I almost feel like I'm trying to get fired from there so I don't have
to walk away on my own. Then I could say I didn't have to choose;
they chose for me. I don't want that, yet I'm struggling."*

Even though that's how my week started, at the end of this week of
programming, I would feel good about where things were at. Thursday after
programming when I got home, I journaled this:

*"Working on the 'inside stuff' isn't about checking off boxes. You
would think a task manager like me would be upset about that,
but it's actually freeing. I don't have to worry about dotting every
'i' and crossing every 't'; I just have to show up four nights a week,
be honest, push and interrupt my eating disorder, and put all my
trust in the good Lord. Because it is happening. I am recovering. I
see it. I'm saying things like 'I don't want another diet in my life.
It was too hard keeping up and created so much misery for me. I
was never happy,' and 'This yogurt parfait is so yummy. Breakfast
is yummy.' I no longer stress about coming up with some 'healthy'*

meal for the week's lunches or some protein-heavy breakfast foods. In fact, I'm no longer stressed about breakfast. It turns out just fine each morning. There has been no need to stress about it. My body is loving me and loving life. It's not craving junk. It's not bingeing. It's not hoarding food. It's not eating in secret. It's not being ashamed of what's in my cart at the grocery store. It's really loving life. This feels so good. So good. Like nothing's going to stop me from recovering!

I may never be under XXX pounds again, and tonight that's okay. As long as I can feel this good about my life, that's all that matters. I do feel like I have a lot to be thankful for. My personal life feels in control for the first time in my adulthood. I am taking care of myself and doing a lot of internal work, and that feels fabulous. I'll continue to make progress and be on to focusing on my career aspirations next. I see how dedicating the time and money toward something really pays off in so many ways. I've got my life back. I'm making small changes and interrupting Ed. That feels fabulous!"

· 8 ·

Wide Open

"When you hold onto the experience as good or bad, the judgment holds you back. Come to terms with what just happened. Neither right or wrong, it just is."
—Jen Nelson, LPCC

 I celebrated a nice, quiet Christmas with my family that first December in programming. Two new books were a special present from my husband; books I really wanted to read. Christmas evening, we visited with my sister Missy and her family, as well as my mom. My soul continued to feel good being surrounded by my family.

My mom brought over a Tupperware container filled with her homemade chocolate chip bars and left it for my family. I had not had one of these bars in years. It was the one food I would eat for breakfast, even though I had always hated breakfast as a kid. They were comforting. Something about home is how they made me feel. These were the same bars my Grandma Jingles attempted to make for my birthday all those years ago.

I remember being the one who my mom would allow to lick the bowl when she was done pouring the batter into the cookie sheet to bake. I seriously could not recall when the last time I'd tasted one was. It had been years.

The morning after Christmas, I ate this long-awaited treat after I had just eaten breakfast. I would journal about the experience. There is so much pain in my words and so many Ed thoughts scattered amongst the words; I just didn't realize it all at the time.

"All my yogurt parfait is gone. I ate bite after bite after bite just now. I could lick the bowl if it wouldn't get my hair messed up and full of yogurt. No one is down here yet, so I take a chocolate chip bar out of the container. First bite reminds me of my mom. Second bite reminds me of our house on Fremont. And now the tears start. I'm not sure if it's the memories or the shame of eating this bar. It does taste good and I want to go eat the entire container right now. They would taste so good. They'd numb these feelings. The thought of my mom being lonely just hits me like a ton of bricks. The tears are flooding out of me. I want to hug her and tell her I'm sorry for all the times I hurt her. Maybe that's me who I'm really crying about. I'm so sorry. I'm so sorry for causing you all this pain. I feel so ashamed. I feel so hurting right now. I just want to love myself and that feels like the hardest thing to do. Always chasing after some other material desire so as to avoid all the suffering.

The tears are drying now. The bar was gone several thoughts ago. It's gonna be okay. The day is still here. I just feel so sad. Like I've wasted away a lot of years chasing after external things/jobs/people to make me happy, and yet I'm miserable inside. Years and years of my own abuse. Years and years of never feeling good enough, so going to chase after everything external to prove my worth. Now I'm a 46-year-old unhappy woman who doesn't know how to be happy, nor how to love herself. It feels like a huge bruise mark. And I feel it on my left side. It's a dull ache. Like it's there, and every so often when I breathe, I feel it. Like a constant reminder of the misery I caused myself. Or maybe I should say Ed caused me. Before I went to get the chocolate chip bar and was thinking back to my grandma making those bars when my mom was away, I thought about the mean boys who called me 'Tick Tock Titty' when I came up to bat in kickball. I can feel the shame – and I was only in 5th grade! My natural curly hair was getting curly, my breasts were blossoming and I'd already started my period. And these boys made me feel terrible about myself. I never feel good enough. Always shy of some award or accolade. I never give myself enough credit. Always chasing. I'm exhausted. I can't keep going

*on like this. I need healing. I need love – self-love. I'm the only one
who can heal myself. What a wonderful gift I'm giving myself."*

As I closed out the last few days of 2017, I was shifted to a new therapist,
Nicole, because Miranda was on maternity leave now. Kicking and screaming
inside, I didn't want to have another therapist to explain everything to. And
Nicole was young and new to her therapy career. I didn't think she would be
any good, and yet she was.

After my first appointment with her, I noted in my journal how I liked
her; she really listened to me and asked good questions. She would ask me,
"What's on deck for 2018?" in that first session. I went on to tell her how
I planned to hire a career coach and get some "work done" as it related to
my career. She cautioned me about the timing and asked if I could take on
something like that in addition to all the internal stuff I was doing. I didn't
think it was realistic I would tell her.

She was not sure if taking on a new job or role was best for me while I was
knee-deep into therapy and IOP. "Until you work on all the internal stuff
and get good there, you will keep running from the uncomfortable to a new
job. Then, as soon as it gets uncomfortable there, you'll run again."

This was an aha moment for me! This was exactly what was happening. It
was like I needed a professional to tell me this, and then I could give myself
permission to take a break on my career searching. It's like I felt lazy when
I took a break to work on myself because I put work and my career on the
back burner. It didn't seem right to focus on me and not my career ladder, yet
it was what I needed. For so long, my career and work were my everything;
they defined me. I was working to divorce myself from this self-image, and
I think Ed really didn't want me to focus on the divorce. He would tell me
to go work on the career stuff so he'd cruise under the radar.

In a way, it felt freeing to put my career on the back burner for now and
finally focus on ME. *So what if I'm an average worker, getting average results?
I'm not trying to be a superstar like I once was, getting "exceeds" on every review
and feeling so ashamed if I didn't. I'm trying to be Teresa Joan Schmitz and
nothing more. I'm trying new things and being assertive and taking care of my
needs. Like Nicole says, if you don't get your foundation built, you'll chuck the*

bad stuff over your shoulder, move to the next job or employer, and then it will all come up again. You won't want to address it, so your stand-by becomes to chuck it over your shoulder and move to another job or employer. Nicole was encouraging me to sit with the uncomfortable. Just let it be. Feel it. Work through it. Let it run its course. It's going to feel uncomfortable and that's okay. She really did allow me to notice how much misery I was in because of chasing after each new carrot that came my way.

Later this same evening in programming, we would have Jen, the Clinic Director at the Woodbury location (and one of my top favorite people at The Emily Program), lead our IOP session. She had us identify our values for 2018 rather than focus on any New Year's resolutions. She would give us each a deck of "values cards," about 50 cards with values on them. She asked us to put them into three piles: not important, important, very important. Then, from the very important pile, we had to pick our top five. *How do I pick just five?* Jen would remind us that these were values, not concrete things; they would evolve over time. I would pick the following values for 2018:

Inner Peace: to experience personal peace
Romance: to have intense, exciting love in my life
Self-Esteem: to feel good about myself
Simplicity: to live my life simply, with minimal needs
Genuineness: to act in a manner that is true to who I am

After choosing, Jen asked us to consider the following questions: How does my Ed reflect my values? How does my Ed block me from achieving these? How do you challenge Ed to live these values?

We had a conversation about these questions and we would talk about tolerating things we may not like. She would suggest that we tolerate any discomfort first. You don't have to like it and you can accept it. "Accepting it doesn't mean you like it or it's okay, it's just acknowledging that it is," Jen would continue to say. She would also tell us to reframe our thoughts and focus on the intention behind the behavior (symptom use) and gently remind us, "We aren't responsible for our first thought, but we are responsible for our second thoughts." This concept would be something that stuck with me for quite some time.

When I got home from programming, Dale was home. I talked to him about the romance value I selected earlier that night when I crawled into bed after my bath. I told him about the exercise and how I selected romance because I wanted us to fall in love with each other again. It felt like we were taking each other for granted and leading our own lives. This was something I wanted to change. I wanted to date my husband, to love him, to not get in a rut or take the other for granted. I wanted to travel and spend time together. I wanted to hold hands. I wanted to take a minute to stand in his arms and not pull away first. I wanted to love him for all he is and all he isn't. I wanted to know him on a deeper level. I wanted to love him unconditionally – the good times and the bad.

The next morning, I would pour out my heart to Dale in a thank-you card. Who knows when the last time I wrote him a thank you card was, if ever. Yet he deserved it. I wanted him to know that I would love him until the day I die. I wanted to create a story together. I didn't want to do life alone and wanted a life-long partner with me.

Later that night in IOP, Jen led us again, and we learned about DBT skills (Dialectical Behavioral Therapy). These are skills I wish someone would have taught me while I was in grade school. These are skills everyone should know. She would introduce us to "wise mind," which is the sweet spot that combines both rational mind and emotional mind. Rational mind is very fact-based, and emotional mind is emotion-led and can end up creating a mountain out of a molehill. It's where our Ed likes to reside. Using a wise mind, we validate the feelings and move forward effectively, such as, "This really sucks, and yet it's temporary." If you are always in your emotional mind, things can become a crisis for you. Start asking, "Does the emotion fit the situation?" Jen would tell us, and "Make sure to do fact checking! Just because you feel it, does not mean it matters."

We celebrated "Friends and Family" night on the last Thursday of December because of the Christmas holiday schedule. I had enough courage to ask Dale to attend. Because Kaitlyn was over 18 years old, she could attend too and was more than happy to come to support me (she was still home from college on Christmas break). Stefania would bring her two good friends. By now, both Brenda and Bonnie were gone from the program, as mentioned in my previous chapter. Addie and Kathryn did not bring any friends or family that night. We had another young girl who had joined our program that week, so she brought her parents. It wasn't long after that night that she no longer attended the program either.

I was nervous about what everyone would think about Dale. He can be opinionated at times and is direct. This was uncharted territory. Jen led the group and Abbie and Katherine were also there to support her. The focus was on communication styles and setting appropriate boundaries. Jen explained how it is better to respond than react and how being assertive isn't always easy and doesn't always feel good. I would journal the following about this evening the next morning:

> *"Last night at Friends and Family, we talked about communication styles and setting appropriate boundaries. It wasn't as bad as last month's Friends and Family session. I had support there – Dale and Kaitlyn – and that felt good. Jen is really good. She's direct – something I aspire to be eventually. With practice I will get there. It was amazing to hear some of what triggers people without boundaries. She said we won't set a boundary until we are ready to. I will work on this, even though it's super uncomfortable.*
>
> *I realize how much internal work I need to do, and yet it feels like I have shed so many layers already. It feels empowering. To take life back by the reins and be in control of yourself and your internal forces. God has truly given me a gift – a beautiful gift that's worth more than any amount of money can buy. I could just pinch myself. This is so incredible. It feels freeing! My only worry is that I'll go back to work and it will all crash and burn. Yet this feels different. This feels permanent. Yet I know nothing lasts forever. And when it fades, which it's bound to, I'll lie in wait for it to bounce back again. Because that's what will happen. Nothing lasts forever. And that's okay. The muck is a necessary part of the journey. Without it, I wouldn't be able to feel this joy. And this joy is so awesome. I will relish in this joy for now rather than worry about when it will crash/end. Joy in the moment. And nothing more. It's that simple!"*

The evening of what would have been my dad's 73rd birthday, Dale and I decided to rent a room at the new Radisson Blu hotel at the Mall of America, just to get away and spend some time together. Here it was only December 30th, and I was already working on my 2018 values! We went to the hotel to get away from life at home and get out of our day-to-day rut. It forced us out of our comfort zone and our usual pattern. We probably spent $400 on the overnight trip, but the time with Dale was worth every penny.

I thoroughly enjoyed the time and experience. It was nothing special, yet everything special. Dinner together. Shopping together. Talking together. Dreaming together. Lovemaking together. Sleeping together. Breakfast together. A quick stroll through the closed mall in the morning together. Enjoying each other's company together. Exactly what my soul needed. I felt fed. It was so good for our relationship, and I captured the following in my journal the morning we were packing our bags to head back home:

"Catching glimpses of Dale over at the chair next to the bed. A beautiful human being. And he's my husband. How I've missed him. I've missed us. Was this all I needed to make the world all right? Because everything seems alright in the world. Like nothing else matters.

Even during lovemaking last night, I felt beautiful. I felt loved. I felt attracted to my husband and wasn't ashamed of any part of my body. I realized how much I missed him. His body. His touch. His kiss. His gentleness. His warmth. His spirit. His soul. Everything about it was just right. I didn't expect anything and got so much in return for letting go. It makes me want more dates with my husband. It brings us together on the same team. As one. We are a team. We are together as one. It makes me realize how much I've missed us. I've spent so much time being alone. And the best thing I needed was to be together, with my soul mate. I didn't realize how much I needed this therapy. He rejuvenated my soul – the inner beauty of me. I feel like an eagle, ready to soar in the wind on this beautiful blue sky and sunny (yet bitterly cold) day. After all these days of gray sky, the sun is out today. I don't think that's a coincidence to what happened to my soul in the past 24 hours. The blanket of gloom has been lifted by bringing in the sunshine. May

I remember how this feels. May I remember when the going gets tough that it probably means I need a good-for-your-soul getaway. Next, I feel ready to schedule my weekend 'silent' retreat. I'm ready to turn inward even more to get this much benefit. I cannot even begin to explain how jubilant this feels. I feel it DEEP in my soul. My soul is shining. The petals on my flower are turned toward my inner rays of light. How amazing it feels to be so connected with your soul. To realize how much your soul needs attention too. So the next time I start wanting to bash my boss or someone else, let me turn inward to seek the truth and light of what is needed."

When we arrived home, life felt lighter. I took a long, soaking, relaxing bath, one I had not done in a long time. My legs were sore and stiff from all the walking at the Mall of America, so I felt like I deserved a bath. It felt good to take that much care of my body. I put bath salts in the water, turned on meditation music and had an ice-cold glass of water on the side of the tub. I didn't even put the washcloth on my tummy – a habit I'd had for years, and a habit that meant I was hiding my body so I didn't have to see it and see how it had changed since my teenage years. Removing the washcloth was an amazing experience. It felt like I was transforming from the inside out.

For so long, Ed made me think it was my job that needed to change. At this point, I authentically knew what I needed: a major overhaul on the inside, and that was happening right before my eyes. I was making it happen. And no change to my body size or shape was needed for this overhaul!

My parents, three sisters, grandparents (my mom's parents), and I at Lake Miltona in summer 1976. I am seated on my mom's lap in the yellow bikini and my sister, Missy is on my dad's lap.

My sister, Missy (on the left), and I at Lake Miltona, my grandparents' lake home, in April 1977. It was nearly 90 degrees out and we had packed no swimsuits, so my mom made us bikini tops with fabric my grandma had lying around and we used our underwear for the bottoms. We had no issues with our bodies back as five- and seven-year-olds!

My sister, Missy (left), and I with the famous big pumpkin mentioned in
Chapter 2. This was the summer of 1977.

My favorite dress from 1980 that included the socks I used to wipe
my nose mentioned in Chapter 2.

This is a photo of my nearly life-long best friend, Heather (right), and I in July 1986 in the Rocky Mountains in Colorado. We were on a road trip with her parents from MN to CO to visit her brother.

Summer vacation in 1983 with my family near the north shore of Minnesota. This is a month after the boys teased me on the playground for my blossoming chest. I was wearing a similar terry-cloth short set as I did that day on the playground. I also have my glasses on in this photo but never wore them to school. I'd go from the third grade until getting contacts in the seventh grade without wearing them to school. I didn't want to be teased.

This is a photo of my parents and I getting ready to walk down the aisle on my wedding day - June 10, 1995.

My son, Ian, and I on Jan 6, 2017, the day I received the call that my son had a plan to commit suicide (mentioned in Chapter 4). This was taken that evening when we played a family game of "Life" to try to comfort all the pain we were experiencing.

This is me after a typical Weight Watchers weigh-in back in 2015 that I mentioned in Chapter 1

Holding seven pounds of fat at my first weigh-in appointment at the Weight Loss Clinic in July 2016 mentioned in Chapter 3. It was the same amount I had lost in that first month of being on an appetite suppressant.

The sight when I climbed out of the car at the scenic overlook to burn my
letter to my dad mentioned in Chapter 2.

The remaining piece of the letter I mentioned in Chapter 2. Doesn't that
look like an eagle's head? No coincidence, I say!

This is the "what recovery means to me" collage I made at The Emily Program that I mentioned in Chapter 6.

My husband, Dale, and I on the beach in Punta Cana, Dominican Republic on March 11, 2020 – all as the world was about to experience a worldwide pandemic, only we had no idea on this day (as mentioned in Chapter 14).

Dale and I enjoying a dinner for two on the beach in Cozumel
as mentioned in Chapter 11.

The trail climbing up to reach the red rock structure in the distance, the one
where I melted down, as mentioned in Chapter 13.

The point when we realized we were not going to make it to the top of Doe Mountain in Sedona as mentioned in Chapter 13.

Ollie, my walking partner, in May 2019.

My sister, Missy (left), my mom (middle), and I on Thanksgiving Day 2017 as mentioned in Chapter 6. The first time I didn't feel stuffed after a turkey dinner. Recovery felt possible this day.

My family of four – Ian, Kaitlyn, me, and Dale

Angie Michel (my friend and producer of my first ever podcast story on *Peace Meal*). I feel lucky to have met Angie. We became friends and can spend many hours in relaxing conversations. This photo is after we spent nearly four hours chatting at a Caribou Coffee shop. Luckily, we were outdoors as they closed two hours prior to our conversation ending!

This is a photo of Heather and I taken at her in-laws' home in June 2021 when she was visiting family in MN. I'm blessed to have such a loyal and dear friend like Heather.

Dale and I at Fenway Park for a Boston Red Sox game in May 2018
when we went to Boston together as mentioned in Chapter 13.

My dear friend, Leanne, and I after one of our dinners together.
This night we didn't close down the restaurant, as we only chatted
for three hours this time.

Three Steps Forward, Two Steps Back

"Recognize the warning signs before the crisis happens."
—Jen Nelson, LPCC

 **I started** the new year (2018) really trying to further my healing, and yet I didn't realize how much healing there was left to do at that point. I don't think anyone does. Just as you peel off one layer, there is more there to peel. On New Year's Day, I journaled the following about the love of my body. This was small progress, and yet was not always consistent progress. Sometimes recovery looks like three steps forward and two steps back.

"I am happy about my body now. It might not be swimsuit model-like, but it's mine and I'm proud of it. I love myself. I really do.

I feel meaning in my current journey. I'm shedding a lot of internal 'weight' and learning how to cope with all the feelings – from extreme happiness to extreme sadness. And all the uncomfortable feelings in between. It's funny how at any given time, it feels like it's the end of the world in the moment of icky feelings. And then when you fast forward a month or two or three, you're thankful for the ickiness!

I'm grateful for my husband, Dale, because he provides me with unconditional love. He supports me and balances me out. He lifts

*me up. He's there when I'm at my worst and at my best. He makes
me laugh and brings me sunshine.*

*I'm also grateful for my two kiddos. They are sunshine on a rainy
day. They are full of life. They are real. They have a unique
perspective. They really bring me joy.*

*I'm also grateful for my experience in The Emily Program. It's like
winning a lottery. I'm learning a lot about myself and my history,
and also about areas I need to work on."*

And just like that, within a few days of returning to work after the new year
and after taking ten days off around the holidays, I was starting a new project
– the project my boss told me I needed to take on during my one-on-one
meeting with her in late November. At that time, I could avoid it because it
wasn't real. Now, there was no avoiding it. On top of this, Kaitlyn would be
heading back to college shortly. Three steps forward, two steps back.

I honestly felt overwhelmed. New things, whether it is a project, routine, or
schedule, create anxiety for me, which then triggers my eating disorder. By
this time, I was using symptoms again: eating emotionally and mindlessly
and sometimes bingeing just to numb from the overwhelm. I didn't want to
ask for help. I didn't want to ask to reduce my hours at work, as I was asked
to take on more. Once again, I felt like I was without a voice. Yet, Nicole
would remind me I needed to set healthy boundaries at work, as I noted in
my journal:

*"Just had a really good session with Nicole. I've got a lot of work
and thinking to do about setting boundaries. She suggested that I
think about what I need first from a mental health/general health
perspective, and then figure out how work fits into that. Does it
mean working 9:00-3:00 p.m. each day so I can work on myself
and my health? This feels uncomfortable. I'm supposed to work
40 hrs/wk and then some. I don't have time to take care of myself.
And I feel guilty about taking care of myself.*

*There is a lot of angst right now. I might have to leave my current
employer or team to find the balance I need, yet I have to ask*

for it first. I need to stand up for what I need. This is 2018. I can't keep living in internal turmoil because I refuse to have tough conversations and do what's right for me, regardless of how that feels. It feels really uncomfortable. I didn't know I was going to have to have these tough conversations to recover. I want to quit just like Bonnie did cuz the going got tough. Yet I'll continue to add to the bag, and the weight is getting unbearable. The pressure cooker is going to explode, as I can't take it much longer. I was fine until I went back to work. There was avoidance of it all while on vacation. That's why I can't wait until retirement, because I won't have to deal with it anymore and can focus on me without conflict. Yet I won't make it to retirement if I don't focus on myself and set boundaries."

That first Sunday of the new year, Kaitlyn headed back to college after spending a month at home on her winter break. I was an emotional mess, in addition to being overwhelmed with the new project at work. After dropping her off to catch her bus, I took a walk. What normally would have been a ten-minute walk turned into 30, as I just couldn't stop crying along the way. It was important to honor my feelings and validate them in this situation though. They were real. Stuffing them with food was not going to help as much as a walk and journaling would. This was progress, even if it felt mucky! Sometimes just writing out your feelings is the biggest step you can take toward recovery.

"I just got back from an emotional walk ten minutes ago. It took me 30 minutes to do. And I cried at various points along the way. I miss my kiddo, Kaitlyn. I know she needs to soar like an eagle and spread her wings, but really? I miss her companionship and friendship so much. She just rolls with life. She doesn't complain. We laugh. We have fun. We spend time together just being. I miss her. I want her home now. She lights up all of my darkest days. Her smile and true companionship is what I miss the most. Her hugs. Her smile. Her calm demeanor. Her caring attitude. Her kindness. All of her.

I am an emotional mess right now. I know it will be better later, but it's just sucky right now."

We also welcomed a few new members that week into our IOP programming, including Leanne, a dear friend. Leanne and I would share how we both sent our daughters back to college after a month break with them at home and how hard that was. I once again felt "normal." Someone else was experiencing the same thing as me. A while later, Leanne and I chatted in the parking lot after programming and realized we had so much more in common than just our oldest daughters being away at college. I looked forward to seeing her, along with my other new friends, each night in programming.

Later, after the night Leanne joined our IOP group, I felt so much sadness from missing Kaitlyn that I binged on Kaitlyn's leftover birthday cake (her birthday was a few days prior) when I got home. Three steps forward, two steps back.

> *"I'm emotionally sad. And Dale is not looking (he's over in the chair in the family room). And I just got home from programming. I heard a sad song 'If We're Honest' on the radio on the way home. Was sad then. Just want to numb the pain and sadness."*

The next morning, I overslept and felt hungover from the "cake fest." Somehow, it felt like payback for a "wrongful" act of bingeing on cake the night before. It was like this hangover was my body's way of rejecting the cake. It continued into the day at work, when I would feel overloaded and like a truck hit me in the middle of my eyes. I wished I could have been at home in front of the TV doing nothing.

At programming that evening, we all headed to Panda Express for dinner with Jen, our therapist, and Katherine, our dietitian. We were told we needed to order an entree, with some form of rice, along with an appetizer. We would order a small serving and were told we had to eat it all. That was the intention of the meal.

I asked if I could get a soft drink. Jen told me to give it a try if there was an intention behind it. "I always get soda with fast food, so let me see if I can drink just some of it and leave the rest." I realize now that it was Ed's voice saying, "I always get soda with fast food," and my own voice saying, "I can drink some and leave the rest." It was how I was trying to live life and conquer my eating disorder at the same time. And it would be successful that night. I would stay engaged in the conversation (Jen and Leanne were at my table) and forget about the soda; I did only end up drinking about half.

That conversation helped me learn so much more about Leanne and Jen, and I wanted to keep talking. I remember my friend Stefania telling me that she wished she was over with us too, as her table wasn't as much fun. We honestly could have stayed there for hours longer; the conversation was that natural. We all like Jen very much. She inspired us, and we held on to her every word.

Two days later on Thursday was my weekly therapy appointment with Nicole before IOP that evening. She and I discussed how I was ready to begin to "wean" myself from IOP. I would transition to three nights the following week, then two nights the week after, then one night and then graduate. I was excited. I felt good about myself and how I had accomplished a lot in those two short months. She suggested taking some time to determine what was next for me and what that looks like.

In this therapy session with her, she made me realize I wasn't feeling overly stuffed after meals or snacks as much, and soda probably has the same power over me as cake. She said Ed wanted me to feel bad about the cake or soda, because then he's in charge. I was looking forward to having my evenings back, doing stuff for myself and growing in my relationship with Dale. One big aha from this session was that setting boundaries felt hard when I did it, but the reward for doing so was me feeling good.

Later, I journaled about three choices with my job. One choice was to stay at my current employer and enroll in a coaching certification program in June. This had the most pros in it, and the biggest, most important, one was that I could finally start following my dreams! Back in the day when I originally enrolled at the University of Minnesota, I wanted to be a social worker. Most recently, I had felt a pull to become a certified coach so I could use my business skills in addition to my God-given talents of being a helper. I had seen the benefits of having a coach myself and wanted to give back in this same way. It was like a calling of mine, 20-plus years in the making. A choice that was a close second was that I could practice setting boundaries at work, followed by the balance and flexibility I was feeling.

At Thursday's IOP, Jen led the group, and we spent time talking about anxiety at length. I suffered from anxiety quite a bit. It was something I can remember having since I was five in Kindergarten. It's when I first started biting my fingernails. This was a group session I really needed. In fact, many people who suffer from eating disorders also suffer from other mental health issues, including anxiety.

When anxiety shows up, we use our eating disorder to cope. And when our eating disorder is no longer there as a coping skill, Jen wanted to make sure we had multiple coping skills in our toolkit instead of just one (Ed). "Your breath is your biggest tool in your toolkit. It's always with you, and no one knows you are using it to cope," Jen said. She also reminded us how the only way to "beat" anxiety was to face it head on. Yikes. This seemed hard for me. I preferred to run when I was anxious.

I had a clear running path outlined in my head any time I was triggered; many marathons had been run on this path. Jen asked us to consider a few things: Is there a certain thought pattern that leads to anxiety? Are there physical symptoms we experience before anxiety? What are your actual thoughts? What are your actual feelings? "When we start challenging our thinking errors, it will give us a hint at our anxiety cycle," she would say.

One famous way I would become anxious was making up stories in my head about what people were going to say or do in certain circumstances. *He'll be mad. He won't understand. She will yell at me. She will fire me. He won't love me anymore. He will divorce me.* The list went on and on. Then, at IOP, Jen said something profound. "What other people think of you, is none of your business," and, "We think we know what's in people's heads, but that's not possible." This is so true. It is not possible to get into someone else's head to determine what they will say or what they are thinking. Impossible. And yet, my anxiety led me to believe it was. *If I practice saying all the right things, I will be able to predict (and therefore prepare) what he will say and do.* I'd spend hours crafting an email a certain way to make sure no one took offense to what I was saying. Correction after correction. And this wasn't the only way anxiety was playing tricks on me.

The other way I would become anxious is by assuming the worst-case scenario and planning for it. It's something I am still working on to this day.

My daughter gently reminds me when I assume the worst today. Jen would remind us that night that if we started to think things could go differently (i.e., positive), you will go in with a better start. Profound.

Friday, to close out the week, I had a career discussion meeting with a senior executive in HR at work. It was originally scheduled for earlier in the month, but she had a conflict and needed to push it out. Looking back, it was a necessary conversation and one that took a tremendous amount of courage for me. My work friend who was in HR had encouraged me to have the conversation with this executive. He helped prepare me, yet I don't think I was prepared for this executive's direct nature. My anxiety was preparing my words and "speech," rather than focusing on using my voice and staying in the moment.

I went into the meeting looking for her to give me an "in" into HR where I thought I belonged, and hoping I would get a mentor or sponsor to boot. She gave me none of that, and yet what she did give me was best for me in the long run. You see, I came in there thinking she would tell me how to transition into HR based on the skills and passions I had. I had spent many previous networking hours looking for this from someone, anyone. I thought I would come out with a checklist of sorts, an easy plan, with all the answers of how to make this goal happen. Instead, she saw right through me. "It's not clear to me what you want. Get quiet in your mind. Only you can determine what it is you want. Only you know your story."

Wow, few people have been so direct with me! I was looking for her approval on something I didn't even need her approval for! Deep down, I knew I really wanted to be a coach. And just because my company didn't have them, didn't mean I was wrong to have these career aspirations. I felt too worried about saying what my true desire was. What would she think of me? Even though I had just spelled out what I wanted after my appointment with Nicole the evening before, I wasn't courageous enough to come out and say it. The time would come. I just wasn't ready at this time.

The next day, Saturday, Dale and I went to our favorite Mexican restaurant in Woodbury (the same one we went to in programming two months prior) to have lunch together and book our Spring Break trip for March. I would openly order a Coke, a regular one, with my meal and Dale would comment,

"You, a regular Coke?" I told him I didn't like the taste of diet soda, and never really did, so I was shamelessly going to have a Coke with my meal. It tasted so good. It was the first time I was openly drinking regular soda (and outside of The Emily Program) and not shaming. Three steps forward…

We booked our trip to Cozumel that day – for just the two of us, something we rarely did. One of us would usually suggest we should include the kids and the other would cave, and yet this time we decided it was a trip for just us. It was long overdue.

Later this same day, I had this reflection:

> *"I want peace and calm on the inside. Only I can do that, and it's not going to be by purchasing stuff. It's going to be by practicing to set boundaries and to really assert what it is I need. My outer world does feel a little chaotic at times, stressful, demanding. And yet that's how I am with myself. I demand so much of myself. I create inner turmoil by changing my mind based on who I'm with or in what role I'm in. At work, I need to have all this power and control. And yet, I don't have that on the inside. It's like a battle behind the curtain; I want what feels good in the moment, yet I feel bad about it after the fact.*
>
> *I've made a lot of progress thru IOP at The Emily Program. I am proud of myself. I did a lot of inner work for ten intense weeks. Now I get to go practice it in the world after I leave the office and don't have programming. I'm excited.*
>
> *I want to experience life and not wait until retirement. My job pays well and provides me flexibility right now. Sure, it's stressful when I need to set boundaries, but that's going to be the case no matter where I am at (employer) or what role I'm in. I fantasized that another company or role would give me satisfaction, when all I really needed was to set boundaries based on what I need. I only needed to give myself permission to let go, to experience life. Waiting 11 years until I retire to travel and enjoy life, doesn't sound good. I want to enjoy this life of mine. I want to relax on the weekends and the evenings after work. My job affords me the*

opportunity to do that right now. Let me just relax and not try to force things to happen…

I want peace and happiness, a great relationship with my husband and a self-esteem that's rockstar level. There. That's what I really want. None of those things is going to come from an employer or role at work. It's all things I can have regardless of employer or role. I'm in control of making those things happen. I can have those things. That's what I really want. I really want to focus on my health and my relationship with my husband…"

Going into Tuesday, January 16, I had no idea it would be the last day of IOP for me. I was stepping down to three days this week, right? Tuesday, Wednesday and Thursday as discussed with Nicole the previous week at my individual therapy session. After that IOP session on Tuesday, I noticed I wasn't learning anything new and really didn't think I needed to step down my treatment like that. So, the next day, Wednesday, January 17, I would make a decision that I didn't know I had the power to make.

At my individual therapy session before the IOP program that evening, Nicole told me I was empowered. She said I had made great progress, and I could make the decision whether or not to continue. It was up to me if the night before would be my last day of IOP. I had no idea I was this empowered. I kept thinking everyone else made the decisions about this process, not me. How very wrong this was.

I am empowered to make decisions for myself and my treatment. For so long, I was waiting for someone to "rescue" me as I often had as a young girl. *Someone else needs to help me since I cannot help myself* is the victim mentality Ed had fed me all these years. *I have no power,* always the victim who needs to be rescued. And the louder you scream, the more attention you will get.

Feeling this empowered felt so freeing that I journaled about it after dinner at home that Wednesday evening. The only slight regret I realized the next morning was that I didn't get a chance to say goodbye to anyone in the IOP program. I knew my three good friends (Stefania, Leanne and Kathryn) would keep in touch with me, but I would never see anyone else again.

"Sitting here writing in my pj's at home was not what I expected when I left the house this morning. I expected to be at another night of IOP . . . I feel free. I've made great progress. All the tools I learned and all the progress I made on the inside is AWESOME! I did all the hard work. I worked diligently for 10.5 weeks at <u>ME</u>. It was hard, yet so worth it. I no longer crave food to stuff my feelings or use to celebrate. In fact, Ed wanted to go celebrate the "good news" with a burger out to eat, but Teresa wanted to go home and veg and process and journal. And just BE. Teresa wanted a good night's sleep. It's a wonderful feeling. I came home and ate what was packed in my lunch box (for IOP that night). It was great to do what Teresa wanted and not what Ed wanted. He still comes along every once in a while, along with Ms. Anxiety, yet I know the truth. My true self knows the truth.

This is really amazing. I take a breath. Pause. Look at my son over in the chair by the fireplace. This is <u>my</u> life. And I'm proud to be in it. Work is going to come and go, but this feeling inside is here. My soul is ignited on fire, and I don't think it can be extinguished. 'This little light of mine, I'm gonna let it shine,' that's what I keep humming right now. I cannot even begin to tell you how this feels. God's given me so much. For that, I am forever thankful.

Like Nicole said today, we spend time daydreaming about some other job and retirement or whatever, instead of living in the now. We dream up these ideas of what our 'dream job' or retirement would be like and fail to see what's right in front of us . . . I'm going to spend the next six months living the life I want and see how that feels. Let me just let go of any preconceived notions of what life has to be. Let me focus on my best version of me — and all that comes with that focus. Simplicity, romance, inner peace, self-esteem, and genuineness are my focus areas for the next 180 days. Let me see how I feel in July. I can only imagine how fabulous I will feel. Ready. Set. Go. Or shall I say, Ready. Set. BE."

As I started to have more time to process since I was not in IOP programming four nights a week, I began to realize the value I had beneath all the layers. I was realizing I was more than an employee at my employer, an IT associate, a mom, a wife. I was a writer, lover, sister, friend, traveler, enjoyer of life, walker, meditator, spiritual being, church goer, prayer person, learner, book reader, sunshine worshiper, nature lover, beach lover, comforter, healer, soul-finder. The list goes on and on. All of these identities made me, me. I am beautiful because of them, as well as without them. No other person is exactly like me. I wanted to identify with all of these things, not just my title at work or my marital or parental status.

Ed wanted me to keep searching for that best job title, that perfect job, that ideal company, so I would be in a state of swirl and discontent all the time. Ed wanted me to love food so much that I would hate my body because of it. Ed wanted me to think I am not good enough. Ed wanted me to lose weight. Ed wanted me to get a new job. Ed wanted me to stay so busy that I would have no time for myself. Ed wanted me to overachieve, to hustle for my worth in external things I do at work. Ed wanted to hold me back. Ed wanted me to validate my every move with others because he thought I was not worthy enough. Ed wanted to word emails ever so carefully so I would get caught in a swirl and need to turn to him. Ed wanted me to be a "good girl" at work and anywhere I was not in charge so he could be in charge when it all crumbled. Ed wanted the swirl, the constant distraction, the constant focus on external validation. With all of this, Ed stays in control.

· 10 ·

Taking My Life Back, One Step at a Time

"Sounds like God is knocking. And you aren't answering the door."
—Jen Nelson, LPCC

 **February** continued with me making progress. Maybe it was more like five steps forward, one step back by now. Or maybe it was two giant leaps forward, one small step back. There was a lot of progress that had been made, and yet body image issues seemed to be hanging on for dear life. The treatment team at The Emily Program would all say body image is the last thing to be healed with an eating disorder. First, you heal your relationship with food. Next, you heal your relationship with yourself and others. Lastly, you heal your relationship with your body. This seems so straight forward, yet it's the deepest healing that needs to be done.

Tremendous progress, yes, but these were the thoughts from a body image war that still raged, as noted in my journal one early February day:

> *"I'm feeling this urge to lose weight today. It feels like it came out of nowhere, yet it feels like it's been there all along, waiting for me to give it attention. I'm feeling like I need to lose weight because my belly has gotten so big, and the biggest reason is because I can feel my upper back as it rolls onto my mid-back area. I've never felt my body feel like this before. It feels like a squishy dough-boy these days. Like it's a way of getting my attention. Even my thighs are feeling squishy in pockets – like a crater, with little divots of*

density. It feels like my body is giving me warning signs. I feel so ashamed for letting myself go and gaining this much weight. I mean, I'm XX pounds heavier than my lowest of XXX in October 2016. I want to be XXX pounds again, not XXX pounds. I mean I don't know what I weigh, but I don't like how my body feels these days. Pants are getting tighter. I must be gaining weight. My knees hurt. My plantar fasciitis is acting up. I love my body, yet it feels like the pain is calling me to action; to lose weight. I am winded when I climb a flight of stairs. Is this how I'm supposed to feel upon discharge of The Emily Program IOP?

I feel like I let myself go and disappointed myself. I'm eating junky/ processed foods and lots of it. I'm eating bigger portions at some meals than I would have in program. I am drinking soda pop almost daily. Something is there about the soda pop that needs to come out and be addressed. It feels terrible doing it. Like it's what's causing me to gain weight. And feel the way I do. It's got such power over me. What is the pop giving me? How about I agree to journal my thoughts and feelings before, during and after my consumption? Even now, at this moment, I really want my 32 oz of Mtn Dew that I get at the gas station each week. Why do I want it? I love the taste. Is it one way of staying out of control and letting Ed rule my world? What am I hanging on to with the pop? What needs to be let go? What is pop giving me? It's like my addiction, like my dad's alcohol. Mtn Dew takes the edge off of things for a short period of time. It tastes good going down, yet the guilt starts shortly after the last sip.

There is so much noise in my head. 'Go on a diet. Here you go again. You completed another program, but didn't change your behaviors or learn the process. You're still eating big portions and drinking regular soda on a regular basis. You've gained a shitload of weight. WTF!' Ed, stop it. You want me to feel bad about my progress. You want to stay in control. You want me to believe progress needs to be a loss of weight. You want me to believe pop is bad. You want me to believe I'm no good. You want me to feel ashamed for going through this program and convincing people I had an eating disorder. You are nasty, Ed. You want me to be *perfect. To only be proud of myself when weighing XXX. To only love myself when I no longer drink regular soda, weigh XXX and have everything together. F*ck you. You suck. You got me in this funk to begin with. I'm not going to listen to you. Go away!"*

My therapist, Nicole, had previously suggested reading a book called, *Healing Your Emotional Self* by Beverly Engel[4], so I would begin reading it a few days after this journal entry. The first "mirror therapy" assignment the author talks about is to notice how often you criticize yourself and to also notice how often you feel exposed, unworthy, or fearful that others will discover how flawed you actually are. There were a few exercises in the beginning of the book, which I noted in my journal on February 3rd:

"1. *'Make a list of all the messages concerning your body that you remember receiving from peers, siblings and friends when you were a child until the present. Include nicknames and insults and things you've been told by friends and lovers.'*

   - *My first recollection of a comment about my body was 5th grade when I was developing and going through puberty. It was spring track and field day. Chris L. said, 'Here comes Tick Tock Titty,' when I went up to home plate during a kickball match/game. I'll never forget it, and it's the first thing that comes to mind about my body.*

   - *I remember going on my first diet and getting 'skinny' in 7th grade when I didn't eat breakfast and ate a malt for lunch every day. Someone commented about how they could see my collarbone, but I didn't think it was a 'bad' thing that it stuck out. I remember how much weight I lost (I didn't think I was doing it on purpose at the time) because I had to get a belt to hold up my jeans. I don't recall how much I weighed, but it was definitely the first time I recall losing weight. It was also the height of a lot of friction at home between my parents and sister.*

---

4   Engel, Beverly. *Healing Your Emotional Self: A Powerful Program to Help You Raise Your Self.* John Wiley & Sons, 2007.

- *I remember not wanting to wear my glasses to school in elementary school and couldn't wait until I turned 12 and could get contacts. I remember needing them in 3rd grade and Eddie P. already had them. He was popular, and the kids in class called him 'Four Eyes,' so I kept not wearing mine. The nurse at school would call me down for an eye check, and I would say I forgot my glasses at home. I'd only wear them at home and just squint at school. I finally got contacts in 7th grade. I was so afraid of being called 'Four Eyes' and being teased that I never wore my glasses to school.*

- *I remember when I was dating Scott in 11th and 12th grade. He would make comments about me eating a patty melt and fries every time we went to Perkins, and yet he'd eat a French Dip and fries all the time. It was like a double standard because he was 'skinny.' I never felt pretty enough or polished enough to hang out with him, his parents, or his friends. I felt like I was a frump compared to them. I lived in St. Paul and they lived in Minnetonka. I didn't have designer clothes like they did.*

- *I remember someone saying I had 'bushy' hair in 5th grade...*

- *I remember being called a nerd in junior high. And a goody two-shoes and a teacher's pet. I was smart and at school that was made out to be uncool..."*

The list would go on and on of all the times I felt not good enough. All the glances into what was probably a lifelong battle with my body, my self-esteem and my relationship with food.

Later this same week, I completed another exercise from the book. The author asked us to look at our face in the mirror and ask *what does your face tell you about yourself?* I would look in the mirror and journal immediately after looking:

"My face has a constant frown from the marks coming down from my lips. I see pain, deep pain, in my eyes. And sadness. A life of sadness. Of regrets. Of pain."

The next question was: "Come closer to the mirror. Look deep in your eyes. What do you see there?" I would again journal immediately after looking:

"I see deep sadness. From the years of not loving myself. Of chasing after everyone else's dreams. I saw tiredness – a life of being tired. Tired of pleasing others. Tired of taking care of everyone else. I see sadness that I missed out on 46 years of living. I see sadness from the years of abuse I gave myself. I see fear. Fear of failure. Fear of not being good enough. Fear of being seen."

The last question in this series had me in tears. The author asked us to take a close look in a full-length mirror and look at your body "not from the standpoint of evaluating it, but from the perspective of seeing what your body says about you:"

"I see a body that craves love. I see a body waiting for a hug. I hug myself. I see a body that was tired and needed love and attention. I see a body who wanted to hide behind closed doors so no one could see me and hurt me. I see so much vulnerability and pain. I see a body aching for love. A body who has endured so much pain and suffering. And abuse. I see a body who is worthy of love and attention. I see a beautiful body, full of love inside. I see a body waiting to be loved and set free. I see a body craving attention."

Later, I journaled about feeling different, in general, with a lot of things, like "five layers of pain and suffering" had been peeled back:

"Kaitlyn will head back to school tomorrow morning after a weekend home, and I'm not as emotional about it as I've been in the past. What's different? What's changed? I feel more at peace inside. I feel like my identity is more than just worker-bee and mom. Sure, it's great to be a mom. There is a lot of enjoyment in being a mom. And yet it's not all what defines me. I am so much more than Mom. The other difference is that it feels like the

cloud of depression has lifted. I don't feel as depressed anymore. The glass feels full, rather than empty. Sure I've got issues with my boss and work, but nothing that's impossible. And now that I don't believe that my job is my sole identifier (besides mom), I feel more alive. I feel like I am more than worker-bee and mom. It feels good. Like I'm a brand-new person in the same body! It's like I peeled back about five layers of pain and suffering and got to the root issue. I've uncovered something pretty big and feel alive. It's like I needed to start loving myself above all others before I could really love others. I was so wrapped up in my individual identities that I really didn't know who I was. It feels good to have these layers lifted. It's like opening a Christmas or birthday gift when it's not even your birthday or Christmas! It's just an ordinary day, Sunday, February 4, 2018, and I have so much more love for myself than I did on February 4, 2017. Who would have thought that a year ago? I was in the middle of a tailspin – Ian's depression, a new job and boss, gaining weight, Kaitlyn's last months of high school, and attempting to find out who I was, but yet not knowing how. I would have never imagined I would feel like this now a year ago...

Fast forward to today. Gone are the commercial diets and weight loss programs thru the doctor's office. Thank goodness! To always be chasing a number on a scale instead of going inside was hard, yet it was the 'easy' answer. 'Just' lose the weight and you'll be happy. I did lose the weight and was happy, yet it only lasted until the scale showed XXX. Then XXX. Then XXX. My happiness was gone the minute I no longer weighed XXX. And I couldn't stand the pressure. I could only eat certain foods and would search endlessly for low-carb, high-protein breakfast meals, none of which I enjoyed. I was eating hamburgers and steaks for breakfast to fill up. I was always making sure I'd eaten enough so I didn't have to snack before lunch. It was like a competition within, and yet it made me so unhappy and tired. I was tired of chasing after another diet that would last until I stopped trying. Then I'd blame myself for not trying hard enough. Now I realize I was doomed to fail the minute I started my first diet ... How could I have let myself go, I thought. Little did I know that I was hurting so much inside, but I did what society teaches you and all I knew, which was to beat myself up for letting myself go...

It was hard, yet I survived by putting all the accumulated baggage into the bag and slung it over my shoulder. Keep going. It's what we do. Suck it up. Pick yourself up and brush yourself off. How could I not do the same? So much baggage. So little self-compassion. So little self-care. All was for the kids. My marriage. Survival at the time. There was so much guilt asking for people to help...

I'm just so happy I still have a life to live. I can't change the past, and I don't want to dwell on it either. I did what I did to survive, and it's all I knew how to do. I didn't know I needed to work on myself. I always thought it was everyone else. Now, at age 46, I'm taking care of myself. It feels good. It feels right, like it was meant to be. I no longer chase after the shiny object, like a diet program or a new job/career. I'm focusing on my insides and making tremendous progress! I'm very proud of myself!"

That weekend, I would go out to dinner with my dear Emily friends (as I refer to them) Leanne, Stefania and Kathryn. It was a good thing I had this dinner planned in advance with them, because it would turn out I would need their support that very night. It ended up being a hard day. At my therapy appointment on the Thursday before, Nicole had suggested that I clean out my closet. I still had a lot of my "smaller" clothes in my closet, which my eating disorder convinced me were for the day when I lost all the weight I had gained since going off the appetite suppressant. I told Nicole how I didn't have many clothes that fit anymore. She would suggest that I get rid of those "smaller" clothes, and then go out and get clothes that fit and I felt good in. I didn't realize how hard this task would be. This is from my journal after completing the task on Saturday afternoon:

"I'm in tears. I've just spent 45 minutes going through my closet and have had to pull most of the clothes out because they don't fit. This is the hardest thing I've had to do. I've let myself go. I've gained XX pounds in the last year. I let myself go. I feel so ashamed. I cannot look at myself in the mirror. I see fat. I see burden. I see pain. I see hurt. I see fat. This is the hardest thing

in my life at the moment to do. So many clothes. So much money. And I've let myself go. I didn't think I had gained that much weight back. I thought I'd get back to about XXX and stabilize there. But the scale said XXX on the day Abbie weighed me. My lowest was XXX. I feel so fat. So unlovable. I've got to stop. The only way to heal is to love myself. This is who I am now. I am still the same person inside. Well, maybe mentally I've changed for the better, but I'm still Teresa Joan Schmitz."

This was the hardest thing I had to do at the time on my journey toward freedom. In my journal entry above, you can see how much Ed came out to attack me in that moment. I was trying on clothes before deciding to get rid of them. That was Ed making me feel ashamed. It felt hard because it felt like my identity was out the window. Hard because there was a lot of money that went into those clothes. Hard because I had already gotten rid of "big" clothes the year before when I lost all the weight on the appetite suppressant. Now, I was doing the same, only in reverse. Up and down like a yo-yo dieter.

It highlighted the pain of never being happy with myself, including my body. Loving your body is not easy. You see so many flaws, yet you know it is the only body you get, and it, too, needs love and compassion to survive. You can't live a full life if you continue to bash your body, and in turn, your soul. Your soul longs for love and acceptance. Once you learn to accept your body as it is, your soul will be free. You can love yourself for all your imperfections.

I will stay awake and fight for my own health and my own needs so my body no longer needs to endure the pain and the abuse. I may never lose a pound again; even so, my body is worthy of love. Every ounce I can smother it with. There is no better love than this. To offer myself the same unconditional love my puppy offers me will set me free.

On Wednesday, February 14, Valentine's Day, my therapist Nicole was out sick, so Morgan called from The Emily Program to see if I'd like to see Jen at 11:00 a.m. instead. *Of course!* I absolutely adored her in all the IOP sessions she led. It was like she had all these treasures of words and wisdom, and I attached onto her every word, sitting on the edge of my seat like you do when it gets to be the climax of a movie in the theater. She was smart. Wise.

Compassionate. Quick-witted. Almost like she, herself, had once been in the bowels of an eating disorder. She never told us this, and yet I often wondered.

Excited to see Jen and get a different perspective, I wanted a pro's perspective, so to speak. I was really restless in the days leading up to this appointment, even though I knew deep down what I wanted. A few days before the appointment, I journaled this:

> *"I'd rather run and hide than go deep inside to ask what it is I need. I'd rather escape than deal with the uncomfortable. I don't know why I'm so restless these days and choosing to escape it all by aimlessly searching for a new job or company. Is it screaming loud and clear that it's time for me to move on? Or is it screaming loud and clear to dig in?"*

It's almost like I knew what I really needed and the restlessness was from all the internal stirring – a longing that my authentic self was no longer afraid to bring forward. More than ever before, I was calling Ed out for what he was saying and doing. Deep down, I knew I wanted to pursue being a coach, but Ed was making me afraid of starting until all things were "perfect."

The therapy session with Jen was awesome. I shared about all of the restlessness, about my current work situation, and my future career desires. I told her how I firmly believed God is in charge and has a plan for me, with everything happening for a reason, and how I kept waiting for a sign from Him. I still remember her response to this day (and probably won't ever forget).

She said, "Sounds like God is knocking." And after a long pause, she finished, "And you aren't answering the door." So spot on. Ed was waiting for the perfect moment, the perfect conditions to pursue my dreams. She told me to move toward a decision. She said that because the fog had been lifted and the eating disorder is not as strong anymore, this desire was coming forward loud and clear. She continued by saying, "Sometimes you just gotta jump off the cliff anyway." So true. See why I say this woman is so full of wisdom nuggets and treasures?

Jen pointed out how I was being black and white in my thinking about work and pivoting into a new career. There were many options to consider, and "It's not all or nothing," she would say. "One option is that you stay there and volunteer outside the company. Another is you stay and take the coaching courses. Another is you work and intern part of the time. Another is you stay in IT and go to an agency that helps people as a company mission. So many different options to consider. You *can* be a coach," she said. I said, "I know. That's what I want to do, but the finances aren't there." "Sounds like you need to challenge some rules you've got going, like not retiring completely in ten years when Dale does and continue to work part time still. Or maybe vacation in the US instead of Cozumel in the future. There are choices," she would say. Jen suggested radically accepting how things were at the moment, because *acceptance doesn't mean you have to like it.*

As we closed out this topic, Jen said Ed had been preventing me from really taking action toward any of this before. I was too dependent on my disease to believe it was me who needed to move forward. Ed wanted me to stay miserable so he could keep me captive. He didn't want me to recover, because I'd leave him in the dust. "It's a lot of work to shift careers," I said, to which she replied, "It's a lot of energy and work to stay miserable."

God, she's good. Spot on again. My friends (who were lucky to have Jen as their therapist) and I still talk about how good she was and all her one-liners. They were revelatory, really making you stop and think. Jen would give me a problem-solving sheet to take home and work on to reflect on this situation more.

During the second half of our therapy session, we talked about my clothes and my attempt at cleaning out my closet the weekend before. Like I mentioned, I tried on the clothes to determine if they still fit; most did not. I still had some drawers to go through, but most of the closet was done. She asked what I would do differently this time with the remaining drawers, and I told her I would not try them on. My main question was *why shouldn't I hang on to these clothes?*

We talked more about this and how I didn't like getting rid of it all or how "big" my body had become. She kept insisting that cleaning out my closet was best for me and my mental health. Because Jen said it was, I trusted her.

Over the weekend, I gave it another try. As we ended our session, I let her know I wanted more time with her. I wanted more "nuggets" of her wisdom.

That weekend, I spent more time cleaning out my closet as Jen suggested. It was not as hard as the weekend before, but I was going into it feeling emotional and not good enough due to a comment someone made to me at work on Friday. I had met with the project sponsor about some project details, and he wasn't happy about something. He told me, "Listen, Doug (the previous Scrum Master before me) was exceptional. You're not Doug. Just be yourself." That stung. I kept hanging on to it. I kept hearing "Teresa, you are not exceptional like Doug was."

I wasn't good enough was internalized. It made me feel terrible about myself. And yet, if I wanted to recover, tackling things head on was needed…even if I didn't want to. I reminded myself that I was good enough and didn't need some project sponsor from work, of all places, to validate me. *They don't walk in my shoes and they don't know my story.* It didn't take away the sting or the emotional toll though.

The rest of the small-clothes purging was done – this time without trying anything on. I would look at the size and make an assumption about whether it would fit or not. Normally, I know sizes vary by brand, yet in this situation and for my own mental health, I could not afford to try on anything. This helped me steer clear of Ed and keep emotionally stable. There were two piles – one with clothes to donate and one with clothes to attempt to sell. I would see them as just clothes this time; clothes Ed wanted me to hold on to so I could torture myself each day, shaming myself for letting myself go. Using my wise mind, I told myself that some of the shirts I never loved anyway, which was honestly true. I ended up with five store paper bags ready to sell at Clothes Mentor in Woodbury and two bags full for donating to the Goodwill.

This exercise felt freeing. In a way, it felt like I was saying goodbye to Ed and moving forward. Ed kept me shopping and accumulating "stuff" so I would be sheltered from dealing with my eating disorder directly. Clothes don't define me and neither does food. I am enough.

I Can See Clearly Now

"Stop apologizing for bumping into someone!"
—Jen Nelson, LPCC

 **Continued** progress. Continued exploration. Critical decision. This is what made up the month of March 2018 for me. At the beginning of the month, Dale and I took our Spring Break trip to Cozumel as planned. We had been there six years prior with the kids and stayed at the same small resort. This time was different. This time we would have all the time to ourselves for five straight days. We would have massages on the beach together and a romantic dinner for just the two of us later that same evening on the beach. It was a time where we really reconnected. Dale works a crazy schedule at his work, so getting time together at home on an average day is tough. Going on this vacation together without our kids meant we could see each other for 120 hours straight.

In the wee hours of the morning before our flight, I woke up grinding my teeth. I don't typically grind my teeth that I am aware of. I am sure it was from all the stress of worrying about leaving my kids at home alone, even though they were 19 and 16 and we had a neighbor friend of mine to help out if they needed it. There was also a snow storm forecasted to dump 6-8 inches of snow in the metro the day after we left. I woke up the morning of our flight with a bad headache. I was really hoping I could relax and enjoy the time away with Dale. *We deserve this trip*, I kept reminding myself.

Because recovery is not a straight line and looks more like a cord from a 1970's avocado-colored rotary dial phone, my eating disorder would show up a bit on this trip. It would show up when I put on my bathing suit for the first time since ending the appetite suppressant program the previous year. It was hard to be comfortable in a bathing suit while in the early stages of recovery. I was spending a lot of time looking at my body in front of the mirror, analyzing every inch before coming out of the bathroom to head to the pool. And then when getting to the pool to do "Aqua Gym" (i.e., water aerobics), I was not staying on my own mat, so to speak, so there was a lot of comparison going on. As we all know, comparison steals your joy. It really does. I could hear Nicole in my head as I stood near the edge of the pool saying, "Stay on your own mat."

My eating disorder also showed up when we ate breakfast at the International Buffet on the next morning after arriving. This was the first time I was eating at a buffet while in recovery. I really wished we had been able to experience a buffet on one of our group program outings in the previous months. This moment was hard, and yet I was full of tools in my toolkit. Sometimes, eating disorders cause you to overthink things, and then it becomes a full-blown issue. This was one of those times.

All this food. It all looks good. And because I was not at home and did not have access to a grocery store or convenience store to purchase snacks, I was so afraid of being hungry on the trip, even though I had brought a few snacks from home in my suitcase. All this food spread out in front of me and my eating disorder attacked me by putting thoughts in my head that I better load up so I didn't get hungry until lunch. It didn't help that my husband tends to overeat at buffets, but then he may not be hungry at all for the next meal. I was so afraid of not having enough that I walked away from the buffet feeling overly stuffed. I made sure to eat enough so I wasn't hungry again, but I *was* hungry later for lunch.

If anything, this experience taught me there were plentiful choices of food, a wide variety that I had access to while on this trip. They would be the same foods available the next day and the next day. I did not need to eat them as if I would never see them again. They would be there again next time, and if by chance they weren't, a new variety of foods would be.

During the first two days on the island, we spent a lot of time at the beach together. We were really quiet; you could tell we had been so used to focusing on the kids for the past 19 + years. We were getting to know one another all over again. It was a good feeling.

On the beach, I would also spend a lot of time reflecting on life. At one point on the second day, I overheard another tourist near me talking to her husband about her daughter. She said, "I told her. Don't overthink it. You know what to do. Just go do it." It totally reminded me of myself. I had wanted to move toward my ideal life. I even knew what that looked like. During my recovery journey, I had spent quiet moments thinking about it. I wanted a simple life. It's why I picked "simplicity" as one of my values of the year.

A simple life meant one with lots of down time, time with loved ones, time to collect my thoughts and time to rejuvenate. It didn't need to be a trip to Cozumel. It could be a trip to get a massage at home, the Como Conservatory, the tropics at the zoo, my backyard, my glider rocker in my bedroom, the library, the front room in my house. As I sat there, I thought about how so many people, even myself, had been looking for mountain-top experiences. Life didn't need to be sitting around waiting for mountain-top experiences. These trips to wonderful places were heaven on earth for sure. There's no denying that, but a simple hand-holding session with Dale at home is heaven on earth too.

During our romantic dinner for two on the beach, we poured over our dreams, our next vacation (we always spent a few minutes talking about our next trip when on a vacation) and of course, our kids. We sat, chatting, really taking each other in. It felt like we were dating all over again. That night would be a top moment of the trip for us both.

We had two excursions booked for the remainder of the trip. The first was a Jeep tour around the island for the day. It was something we had done before with the kids and really enjoyed it, so we decided to do it again. To tell you the truth, this time around was not the same experience. We had another couple in the Jeep with us (strangers), and it was awkward. The sights were still beautiful, but it was just not the same.

The second excursion was a snorkeling trip on a catamaran. I don't know how to swim (I almost drowned when I was a child, so I have been afraid to put my head under water ever since). After our trip, I decided to sign up for swimming lessons at the local YMCA, but continued to refuse to put my head under water. The poor young teenage instructor…he told me he had always been successful getting people to overcome their fears when it came to swimming. I was his first failed case. He thought it was because I had waited too long after the incident to overcome my fears. "Your parents should have forced you to take lessons right after that incident so you would have overcome the fear. It's been too many years," he said.

On the catamaran, the excursion staff asked me over and over why I didn't want to snorkel. I would politely decline their offers and opt for sitting on the top deck to sunbathe. I could see Dale snorkeling below and could still capture sights of the beautiful turquoise waters below. I was fine. Not everyone likes to snorkel. I really was enjoying myself. After all, I was near the water with Dale and was in the sun on a boat. These are three of my favorite things. At one point, I texted Stefania, Leanne and Kathryn a photo of a nearby catamaran. It was a boat of about five women who appeared to be celebrating life together. I told them how we should do that sometime together.

I really went into this trip with no expectations. Back at home, contemplating this made me realize how I like things to be so planned out in my day-to-day living. Then I get disappointed when things don't go according to plan. When you just go with the flow and let life unfold before your eyes, there's no turning back with regrets. I would capture this a day after we arrived home:

> *"There is calm. Maybe that is the biggest lesson I learned on this trip that God needed me to learn first-hand. I spend hours worrying about a career, my weight, my clothes, having control over when and what will happen in my life…that I'm a walking worry-wart. He's the one in charge. Let life unfold in front of me. Life is gonna be okay. I can feel it. At this moment (and even packing up my bags the other night at the hotel), I have no dread about having to go back to work (or home as it was the other night). There will be more time off. There will be more escapes away from home and work. Another thing this trip taught me was*

the importance of placing a priority on our relationship. Our lives
will be abundantly wealthy because of that exercise of spending
time together. All 'free' for the making, and yet so rich in reward."

The following Tuesday after vacation, I would start DBT (Dialectical Behavioral Therapy) skills group at The Emily Program from 4:00-5:00 p.m. every Tuesday. Along with a few others, my three friends would be there – Stefania, Leanne. and Kathryn. Jen told us it was at least a six-month commitment, unlike IOP that was only 10.5 weeks for me. It was only one night a week though, and only one hour a week. I was so glad Jen was teaching it. I liked her. I admired her assertive style.

Even though she had taught DBT for ten years, it was a muscle she still practiced daily, she told us that first night. DBT is based on mindfulness, so we spent that first evening learning all about mindfulness. At first, I thought it was going to be easy, and yet just like anything of worth, DBT skills will take a lot of practice. Later that evening, I journaled this about my first DBT session:

"I had DBT class with Jen today and learned a shitload. I learned
that the road to recovery is going to mean mindfulness. It's going
to be non-judgmental judging about feelings and thoughts. For
example, it will mean acknowledging I am restless. And that is
neither good nor bad. It just is. Wow! I can't wait to be able to get
there. I don't like the uncomfortableness and the silence, and I do
everything but sit with them and feel them. I think I need to work
on this. It's gonna be hard not to judge my thoughts and feelings
and to just let them be what they are without trying to change
them either. It's not good or bad that I am restless. I'm restless. In
the future, I can name the emotion I feel in the moment if I'm
in the middle of something else, and then carve out time later to
feel the feeling. I'm avoiding feeling the restlessness, I mean really
feeling it, that I'm stuffing it with something else in hopes it will
go away. It is not going to go away magically. It needs to have its
own time to be felt — without attachment or judgment or trying
to change it. It's restlessness. That's it. Nothing more. Nothing less.
I really don't know what it <u>really</u> feels like to feel uncomfortable. I
think I should explore what that feels like."

One key concept we learned in DBT early on, in addition to the mindfulness piece, was something called DEAR MAN. We had talked about it during IOP, and yet I don't recall specific times of using it while in that group. I am sure I did, it's just not as clear as the first time I used it during DBT. DEAR MAN is all about having assertive, direct conversations with someone else when you want them to know how you feel about something. I got practice right away after learning the skill in DBT.

I had been working with someone who was a relative of someone in my professional network. We met over the phone, as I was looking for someone to redo my resume. We talked for about an hour, and then agreed to meet again. At the end of the second call, he told me I owed him $500 as he charges $250/hr, and he had spent about that much on researching in prep for redoing my resume. *Say what?* We had never once had a conversation about paying him for these services, and this was the first time I was hearing this.

I was afraid to tell Dale about this situation, thinking he'd be mad when I told him about it. He said he was disappointed that I thought he'd be mad when I told him. There I was, practicing my famous mind-reading skill again. I would continue to work on fact-checking my thoughts like this in the future, and I would practice my DEAR MAN conversation I was about to have with this individual.

I was proud of how it went. I told him we had not discussed payment in the two conversations we had had before, so I had assumed he was not charging me. We agreed on a dollar amount comfortable for both of us, then I ended the call. This was the first time I was assertive in a conversation that I normally would have avoided at all costs. In the past, before recovery, I would have become resentful at this person and paid him what he originally asked me to pay. The resentment would have continued for years. And yet, it didn't. *I am so proud of me in this moment.*

Near the end of March, I would make a critical decision – one that would turn out to be one of the best decisions I've made for me. Many years in the making, I was finally moving toward my dreams; toward something I had wanted for so long, but was waiting for someone else to validate it as a good decision. On Saturday, March 24th, Dale and I talked at length about my desire to pursue a coaching certification. The first part of the training would cost $1,695, and since Dale and I had a rule to discuss making any big purchases, I knew I needed to discuss it with Dale. I used more DEAR MAN skills when having that conversation, and at the end of it, Dale agreed that it was a good decision for me.

I signed up for coach training that same day! I was exhilarated. It was like a ton of bricks had been lifted from my shoulders. I was doing something for myself, by myself. This was incredible! Interestingly, the song "I Can See Clearly Now" by Johnny Nash kept playing over and over in my head in the days leading up to that Saturday, and now I know why!

· 12 ·

Breaking Free

"A lack of boundaries breeds a lack of respect."
—Jen Nelson, LPCC

 **About** a week after signing up for this coaching program and being so excited and "clear," I had an appointment with my dietitian, Abbie. Because I was making a decision to pursue my dreams of coach training, my eating disorder came back with vengeance. It reared its head to provide me "comfort," a sense of peace, since I was doing something that was not my typical self. My eating disorder had me focused on how my clothes didn't fit, and therefore, I was not worthy and needed to stay attached to him at the hip. He wanted me focused on the weight and my body, rather than the joy of pursuing my dreams. I journaled about how I felt later after the appointment (keep in mind at this time, I was still gaining weight as I had been fully weaned from the appetite suppressant and my body was responding to the starvation it had endured for 1.5 years prior):

> *"Ed feels like he is back with vengeance! My pants are too tight again and my sweaters are too short, so I have to go buy yet more clothes. I feel like this revolving door! Every two months, I am out shopping for stupid pants! I feel like Ed wants me to stay miserable with work, so he doesn't want me to make progress toward freedom. He keeps pulling me back. I want freedom. I want a good way forward. I don't want to be tied to Ed for a lifetime."*

A few days later, I would journal more about my eating disorder and trying to break free:

> *"We got an inch or so of snow overnight. Winter is hanging on tight and does not want to let go. It's like my Ed that wants to hold on tight to me and not let go either. Having an Ed is hard. He wants you to hang on as long as possible so he can be in charge. He wants you worried about your weight and pants being too tight. Cuz if you focus on that, you'll tell yourself you need to lose weight and turn to food to comfort you. Ed is sneaky. He lurks in your pants buckle, in your jacket zipper and your underwear. He waits to lunge out at you when you are vulnerable. Then, he latches on like head lice, not letting go, hanging on for dear life, not wanting to give any control back to you."*

As I mentioned, one of the key components of DBT therapy was about mindfulness. By April 2018, we were a few lessons into mindfulness when we were assigned to do a simple activity: practice mindfulness in an everyday activity. Since bathing in the tub would sometimes lead to a shame fest, I decided to complete my homework on mindfulness while taking a bath. I would journal about the experience afterwards:

> *"I just spent 25 minutes in the tub, in slow motion, doing the mindfulness exercise with a bath. At first, I found it to be hard to settle into the tub without wanting to just wash up and get out. Then, I got super-hot, but fought off the urge to give in and get up from my relaxing pose. I tried tuning in and was successful. I noticed my breath was shallow because I was uncomfortable. I wanted to fight the urge really bad. It was like being in a strait jacket with your hands tied behind your back, and you have an immensely itchy spot on your leg you can't reach. So hard. You cannot reach it. You feel out of control. And then, you realize that calming yourself is in your control, so you breathe in and focus there. In, out. Suddenly, you forget about being uncomfortably hot. You relax. And then, your mind gets busy and you come back to relaxing more. You mindfully take a drink of cold water, and all the worries and uncomfortable feelings fade away.*

Then, because this is your first run at flexing this muscle, you begin to think about actually washing your body. You take the bar of soap and scrub it into the washcloth. You run the washcloth onto your left arm and take your right hand and touch your body. Gently. Like a mother caresses her newborn child in a loving way. You've never felt this touch before. It feels soothing. You do it again. You realize how much your body needed this loving touch, and you were the only one to have just the right touch.

You cannot believe you deprived yourself of a soft touch, and an 'I love you' whispered to your own body from your own lips. You hang on tight. Wanting more. You cannot believe how much you have missed and longed for your own precious self-love.

You do the same to the other arm. It feels so good. You've needed this. You hug yourself with your right hand over your heart and your left hand over your tummy and you whisper, 'I love you, and I am listening.'

I feel so loved right now. I feel like I gave my body love and attention. For free. And by myself. It's a tremendous feeling. I want more of this. I am going to continue to tune in. When I am uncomfortable, I am going to breathe in and out until it passes. I am going to notice. Here's to continued exploration and progress!"

The following week, I would have DBT class again on Tuesday after my weekly individual therapy session. I captured how important it was to put myself first by having important conversations with people in my journal later that evening:

"My therapy session felt intense. I don't know if that's because I left feeling overwhelmed or what (we talked about the Dear Man conversations that were necessary for me to have). Then, class (DBT) was good, yet brought up the conversations I need to have again. I've never really asked for much my whole life. Standing up for myself and my needs feels like I'm asking for too much. I just want to run and hide. There are about four different Dear Man conversations I need to have, and yet I just want to avoid. Ed

> *wants to call in sick for about a week and just avoid and eat. He is LOUD!!!!! Yet, I know the road to happiness and authenticity is having each and every one of these conversations. It's all for the better. There is no getting around that. Maybe because I've always been able to just take a class and pass the test without having to implement into my life is how it's been for 46+ years. Now, if I want to recover, I've got to pick up the pieces and implement what we learn and talk about each week. This is hard stuff. And yet, I know I'm worth it."*

In mid-April 2018, I took two consecutive sick days from work and wrote about the inner turmoil in my journal. In all my years in school and the working world, I barely called in sick. Even if we were given a certain number of sick days, I never used them. I felt like being gone was a sign that we were not loyal or dedicated, and that we were weak for needing to take time off to rest and recoup. Accolades for perfect attendance was what I wanted, even though they stopped giving those out in elementary school! By this point in my journey, it was still a little bit of an inner battle:

> *"Yesterday, I stayed home from work. I needed it. Today, my head feels disconnected from my body. I may need another day to rest and recover. It's funny how I used to not stay home to take care of myself. I'd go to work or school because I didn't want to miss anything. It was always hard taking care of my different needs. And yesterday and today feel no different.*
>
> *My head feels disconnected from the rest of my body. My body just wants rest and relaxation, and I want to give myself that. Yet, a part of me feels bad for being out again. There is work to do. Yet, I feel like if I took care of myself, I'd recover faster.*
>
> *Why do these things have to be so hard? My body needs rest and recovery. It feels like a Mack truck hit me. And I don't have much energy. And the only thing I want to do is go back to bed. I'm worried though. I was supposed to have my conversation with my boss about my class. If I don't go to work today, it will get pushed to another day. I've got to take care of myself though."*

A few weeks after staying home to take care of myself when I was physically sick, I would have my yearly gynecological exam with my OB/GYN doctor; the same OB/GYN I'd been seeing since 1998 when I became pregnant with my daughter. My mom started seeing this OB/GYN when she had a cancer diagnosis in 1996, so I thought I should select her since she knew my family history. This OB/GYN doctor was always focused on my weight. Every doctor's appointment I had with her was about the weight. "It's easier to lose weight in your 20's vs. your 30's," she would say. Then, the next decade hit and it would become, "It's easier to lose weight in your 30's vs. your 40's." Then, when I started going through perimenopause in 2014, she told me, "It's easier to lose weight before menopause vs. after. Just ask your mom." She was so excited whenever I dropped weight and would tell me to, "Keep it up."

She was not there in 2017 for my yearly appointment, as she was called off to deliver another patient's baby, so when I saw her in 2018, it had been two years. Yet, she still had access to my weigh-in record for that 2017 appointment with the Nurse Practitioner; the record that showed I was down 10% of my weight from my time in 2016 because I was on an appetite suppressant.

I'll never forget that appointment in 2018. I was sitting in the room, naked and wrapped in a paper-thin gown. I could feel my tummy and round chest rubbing together underneath that thin layer. I dreaded seeing her, knowing she would comment about my weight. And this appointment was no different, other than she humiliated and shamed me unlike ever before.

"You've gained how much? No way. That can't be," was the first thing out of her mouth as she entered the room with her laptop in hand. No *hello, how have you been?* No *it's good to see you.* Nope, straight to the shame fest.

When she finally stopped with the shaming, I meekly told her I had been diagnosed with an eating disorder seven months prior. I expected her response to change to one of compassion. It only got worse. "I don't mean to be insensitive, but that's a hell of a lot of weight gain. Did you really gain that much weight in the last year?"

I held back tears. I felt so humiliated. And shocked, quite honestly. *How can this doctor be talking to me like this?* We would continue with the exam, and she walked out of the room saying something about how I would be down a bunch of weight when I saw her next because I am in treatment now. Looking back, I should have stood up and left, yet when you are naked and living in a body you, yourself, already hate, it's not exactly the easiest thing to do. Somehow, you feel like you deserve it.

As I drove home, I realized how much she triggered me. By now, I was thinking that I needed to go on a diet again. I felt so humiliated and ashamed. I went home and wrote her a letter in my journal, telling her how insensitive she was and how she needed to be trained around eating disorders. I felt better. Although I never sent her the letter, I did call the office the following week to ask for my records to be released because I was finding a new doctor. That felt empowering in and of itself.

I'm happy to say I found the world's best OB/GYN to replace her and have not regretted it one bit. I only wish I would have found the courage to find a different doctor after her first comment about my weight back in 1998. My new OB/GYN cried with me when I told her (at my first appointment) about the experience with my previous doctor. She said, "You should never have to feel like that with a doctor. I'm glad you came here."

After the shameful appointment, I was just a little over a week away from a "silent retreat" I signed up for in January with my sister, Missy. When I signed up for it in January, I was excited. Yet when the day had come to spend half a day in the middle of May, when the weather is just turning nice here in Minnesota, at the University of Minnesota Center for Spirituality and Healing, I was feeling a little like it would be a waste of time. It turned out to be the best medicine I needed at the time, as I noted in my journal the following day:

> *"Yesterday, I went to a four-hour Mindfulness Retreat with Missy. At first, I was upset that I was "wasting" half of a Saturday going to this. I was resentful for signing up. I was tired and crabby. Yet when I got home, I felt rested. Like I'd taken care of myself, deeply, for the first time in years. My body thanked me. My mind and "doing" attitude stomped her feet a little because not much got*

"done" in that time away from home. In fact, I was antsy to leave about two hours into it. I had a hard time shutting off my mind. I thought often of the time as "wasted." Then, something shifted in me. I got this time with my sister and my body needed it. It's easy for the mind to "feel" good all the time since we are "doing" all the time, or so it feels. This was the first time I gave my <u>body</u> four full hours of a retreat and focus. I felt very rested driving home vs. the groggy feeling I felt driving there. It was as if I let something go while I was there and didn't even realize it. Maybe it was the Qigong exercise we did at the end where we blew everything "bad" out of us. I don't know, but I felt rested, extremely rested."

· 13 ·

Navigating Recovery

"Who said it had to be perfect?"
—*Jen Nelson, LPCC*

 **Shortly** after this silent retreat weekend, Dale and I took another trip in late May 2018. This time, we went to Boston for five days over the Memorial Day weekend. It was time to start living my life. Before treatment and recovery, I kept thinking about retirement. I imagined it as the time when I could start enjoying life and really living. In recovery, I learned that I can enjoy life no matter what stage of life I am in. Why wait until retirement to travel, to live, to thrive? I don't have to wait until I am in a certain body size or shape to thrive either.

We truly enjoyed ourselves on this trip. Neither of us had ever been to Boston before. We did a lot of walking and a lot of sightseeing. We took the ferry over to P-town (Provincetown, MA) where we could get out and explore the town, the sand dunes by jeep and the waves crashing to the shore. It was much more laid back than being in the city. We spent morning, noon and night in each other's presence. It was so healthy for us to do this and such a gift.

Each Tuesday that spring and summer, I continued to join my DBT group at The Emily Program. I would occasionally go out to dinner afterwards with Stefania, Leanne and Kathryn. We were becoming good friends by now and had so much in common. Even though all four of us had the same eating disorder diagnosis, we each brought a unique perspective to both the eating disorder and our recovery. We really enjoyed the DBT group and all we were learning.

In July 2018, I started my coach training program online. It was the best decision I had made for my own career development since going to college and pursuing a social science degree, despite my dad's plea to pursue a science or math degree because I was "good at it." On that first night of coach training, I recall thinking, *I have chosen the right path. I don't have to force myself to like this. It comes so naturally for me.* My soul was really on fire. It was like it was coming full circle now. I had gone to college to become a social worker, and while a life coach is not at all a therapist, it felt like it was meant to be. I had a real-life experience and was seeing the benefits of having a life coach.

I began coaching people that same summer. At first, I was trying so hard to ask the right questions, it seemed like I was not staying in the moment. Over time, I would get better at staying in the moment *and* asking questions in the moment. I started showing up better at home and at my corporate job too because of the training and coaching I was both providing and receiving.

For a full year, I stayed in DBT and attempted to use the skills we were learning with Jen each week in my day-to-day life. There were periods of ups and downs for sure. I would get real practice with Dear Man, Behavior Chain Analysis, Self-Compassion, Radical Acceptance, and Urge Surfing when I moved into a new role at my corporate job in early 2019.

At the beginning of 2019, I moved into a role in IT that I had never been in before. My boss had a conversation with me about three months prior, and when a new role popped up under him, he asked me if I wanted it. I didn't have to interview for it, yet I didn't even understand what my expectations were at the beginning, so I would have a lot of Dear Man conversations with my boss to get better clarity. When he wouldn't provide the clarity, I would ask again. Sometimes, I would sound like a broken record. (For those who have not heard of Dear Man before, it's a great communication framework to use for assertive conversations. D = Describe what you want. E = Express how the situation makes you feel. A= Assert what you need to say. R = Reinforce your desired outcome. M= Stay mindful so you don't get sidetracked into harmful arguments and lose focus. A = Appear confident – eye contact, body language, etc. N = Negotiate – be open to negotiation.)

When he asked me to take on more responsibility just two months into the role, I recall starting my Dear Man conversation with, "I am smart. I am learning. And I am overwhelmed." I really wanted him to understand how I had too much on my plate already and it was way too soon to be telling me to take on more responsibility. I could barely stay afloat with everything I already had. The eating disorder wanted me to just take it all on and be resentful later when I collapsed. My authentic self said *no way*.

This was a constant battle for about six months, so while I was in recovery at this moment, some of my symptom use returned a bit for a short period of time. My therapist would remind me that this was normal. Remember the 1970's phone cord all tangled up in a ball...but I kept showing up, sitting in the hard emotional mess, day in and day out. I knew deep down it would eventually change. And it did. The more Dear Man conversations I had with my boss, the less I feared him or asking for what I needed.

Sometimes, I would not have enough courage to ask for what I needed early on. I was really struggling with staying on top of this new role and continuing in my recovery. One night, I journaled how I thought God had abandoned me, and so I used McDonald's to cope over having a Dear Man conversation. My go-to solution had become leaving the grayness and ambiguity of my new role behind, and seek out a new role (how absurd, right?). I now recognize this thought process as being when I need to take a step back and ask myself *what is really triggering me?* Then, address it directly. Most likely, it is being triggered by needing to ask for help or having a crucial conversation with someone, like I noted in my journal one night:

> *"Lord, I need You. I really need You. I feel like You abandoned me when attempting to find courage when talking to my boss. I didn't find my courage. I didn't find my voice. What is it You are trying to teach me? I know You really didn't abandon me. I just felt alone. I feel like speaking up is hard. I feel it in my shoulders more than ever. If anything, I realize how I turn to Ed when I feel like I didn't speak up. It's a shameful thing. Like I let myself down. And to be honest, it felt easier not saying anything than trying to*

express what it is I needed or wanted. And it felt super comfortable to just eat McDonald's and a 32 oz. of Dr Pepper rather than dealing with how uncomfortable I was. And it hurts real bad. Because part of me doesn't know what the hell I want or need, and all of me does not want to ask. It's easier to avoid. And avoid. And avoid. I'm the only one who suffers. No one else suffers. I want the old Teresa back who just avoids and eats when avoiding hurts too much. I just don't know what the hell I need. It just feels like I want a get-out-of-jail-free card. I want to just move on, yet I want to feel free. I don't know what the hell to do. Is it best to wait until next week or try to talk to him tomorrow? Or just say f*ck it? Let it all work out/shake out, and I'll just do what I can do. He's not clearly defined what it is I should be doing anyway.

Lord, please help me. I am struggling and need Your loving hand to hold me up. I feel like I'm falling down and can't get up. Please help. Please help me, Lord. I want You to find me another opportunity to go elsewhere. Please. I don't want this job. I don't want the stress. I want to feel content. I want to just love myself, no matter what. I'm trying to make pretty big changes, and it's hard work. And I want different results right away without having to do anything different. Help me. I can't do this without You."

It wasn't long after this journal entry, that I would begin to realize I was causing my own suffering. I was letting my anxiety and my eating disorder run the show early on in this new role. My anxiety was promising me utopia in a new job, a new career, or a new life. She lured me to believe her line of bull, so much so, that I couldn't stop ruminating on her thoughts and ideas. Her volume was so loud. I recalled how I had read Dr. Kristin Neff's *Self-Compassion* book, in which she says:

Pain x Resistance = Suffering

I would realize that maybe God was gifting me this situation to build resilience and practice all of what I was learning in DBT group. Everything isn't going to be rosy all the time. There are going to be tough times. Life is going to throw punches your way on a daily basis. Running from the problem is not an effective solution, unless it's a tiger trying to attack you! Running from the problem only prolongs the problem and delays healing. You never get to recover and heal when you run as you avoid until it happens again. Then, you avoid again. And again. And again.

I gave myself some space and time to get through this period. I offered myself compassion so I could eliminate my own suffering and eventually begin to radically accept things as they are. My therapist, Nicole, even suggested that I stop trying to overachieve like my old self and give up looking for a job or meeting with people who would trigger my desire to move to a new job. "Give the job you have a sense of settling in." I sat in the muck and knew eventually I would make it out. I would remind myself that being a little afraid, giving the Dear Man conversation a try and not having it go so well was better than doing nothing and expecting something to change. In a way, it felt freeing. I was giving myself permission to reduce my own suffering. What a novel idea!

In late March 2019, I would graduate from my DBT group, along with my friend Stefania. We started IOP together 16 months prior, and now we were graduating DBT on the same day together. This was a BIG step. We both got to select a rock from the basket and have the other group members give a little speech, including Jen, our DBT therapist. The words on the rocks did not resonate with me, so I took a blank one and wrote "Courage" on one side. I felt I had gained a lot of courage in the program and would need a lot to continue. My friend Stefania hand-wrote the word "Thrive" on her rock. She inspired me so much in her own journey. So much so, that I would write "Thrive" on the other side of my rock the very next day. I took that rock into the office and proudly displayed it on my office desk at work. It is a great reminder of how far I have come; it takes a lot of courage to live a life where you are thriving.

I cried as the others in the group spoke about me and my strengths. I was bawling when my friend Leanne spoke and could barely see out of my eyes when Jen spoke last. Such kind words, many of which I could not remember when trying to write in my journal that night:

> *"I graduated from DBT tonight. It was an emotional goodbye. I cried. Jen cried. She said beautiful things about me. Everyone in*

the circle said such nice things about me as they passed around my
rock – Hannah, Alex, Leanne, Stefania, Kathryn, and Jen. I wish
I could remember it all. I chose courage for my rock. Jen told me
Brené Brown talks about courage and showing up and being a
warrior. She said I am a warrior. And that she's seen me do things
I didn't think I could do. I'm gonna miss her."

A couple weeks after my graduation, Stefania, Leanne, Kathryn and I decided to meet at The Tavern Grill in Woodbury one evening to have dinner together. Since we were no longer in DBT together, we missed each other. It was exactly what I needed, as I would journal the very next morning:

"I am filled with abundant joy. I have amazing friends who I met
through The Emily Program. Leanne, Stefania and Kathryn are
friends who get me. They get the disorder. They can offer me good,
solid advice unlike others who have not walked in our shoes. I feel
so blessed. So full of joy knowing them.

The four of us went out to dinner last night. Leanne offered me
so much good advice. I told them about my desire to always want
to escape from my job, and how I keep thinking a new job will
solve everything. Leanne said, "This shit will follow you." And it
wasn't in a bad way. She is right. I have issues. I discovered that
I look for validation from my bosses and others that I am doing a
good job. And because I don't get it often, I want to leave. Leanne
suggested that I put little positive affirmations around at my desk.
Ones that speak to me. Things like I am smart. I am capable. I
can ask for help. They all seemed to roll off her tongue so easily.

I also discovered I'm super lonely at work and need more connection.
She made a couple suggestions about connecting with others or
spending a day over at our corporate headquarters building a few
blocks away from my own building.

She also said something like, "I'm the captain of this ship," when
talking about doing what brings you joy. We talked about how this
stuff will continue to haunt me at the next job until I deal with
it and work through it. We talked about how I don't believe in

myself enough so I seek external validation. That I need to say this new mantra or positive affirmations, but that the most important thing is <u>believing</u> in them. I can't say them just to say them. I must believe them. And slowly, I'll rely less and less on my boss or others for external validation.

So incredibly helpful to have these ladies in my life. They are compassionate and honest. It's what a great friend should feel like. I love how I settled on staying in this job and doing the internal work. I determined that I can work on myself and my internal stuff over the next few years, so when I coach people, my own garbage does not get in the way."

When I got home from this dinner with my friends, Dale and I booked another trip that we had been wanting to take for some time. A while back, we had decided we really wanted to take another trip together, just the two of us. We had not been anywhere since we went to Boston in May 2018, so we booked a trip to the Grand Canyon for the upcoming October – five days and four nights in Arizona. We booked it for a time when we knew our son would be home for an extended weekend due to some teacher conference days at school. He could stay home and take care of Ollie for us.

A few weeks later, I would have an EMDR therapy session with Nicole that would bring forward some very vivid images of my childhood. I recalled being at the spelling bee and spelling "jerk" incorrectly and my mom's reaction. The memory of the boys teasing me on the playground on track and field day in 5th grade came up. I recalled my junior-high school band teacher who had explosions during class at times. Then, I would move to the first few months of my marriage with Dale, and most recently, my boss.

That night after therapy, I had a dream about work and would wake to think I was hearing someone saying, "Mom. Mom." But the house was as quiet as can be, and neither kid was around (Kaitlyn was in Mankato and Ian's bedroom was in the lower level of our house at this time). After getting myself ready for the day, I settled into meditation and journaling as usual before going downstairs. I think God was trying to get my attention about fear that morning, as I noted in my journal:

"I AM GOOD ENOUGH. AND I AM CAPABLE!

These were the two themes that came out of my EMDR therapy session with Nicole yesterday. I shed a lot of tears. SO many stories that my brain connected with a common theme of never good enough. Before I woke up for the day, I heard someone saying, "Mom. Mom." I wonder if it's carry over from my therapy session, in which I was back as a kid again at my 3rd grade spelling bee, disappointing my mom because I spelled the word "jerk" incorrectly.

This is a little eerie…I went to go fix my contact lenses after writing the word 'incorrectly' above. I paused my meditation music that was playing on Insight Timer. When I came back and lifted my headphones to my ear again, "Fear is a Liar" by Zach Williams was starting to play from my iTunes! I think God wanted to remind me I am enough. That fear will continue to stand in my way until I trust in Him wholeheartedly.

Lord, thank you for giving me life; for giving me this day. Thank you for putting all Your love, faith and trust in me. Thank you for giving me the good, bad and ugly. I realize You just want me to be Yours and to be the best version of myself. Maybe all this muck is there to set me up for something in the future. Or maybe it's there for me so I can move forward now. I don't know and I'll never really know, yet I can trust in You and know You know what's best for me and You know what you're doing. Thank you, Lord. You are moving me in ways I never thought possible. You've allowed me to slowly recover from a major mental health diagnosis. You're allowing me to continue to recover and are there every step of the way! You are amazingly good, even in all the muck.

I'm ready to move forward and become a better version of me. I am capable. I am enough. It's all worth it. I am clearing out all my emotional baggage. I am glad I get to start moving forward with my life now. It's mine to love, and God wants life to be freeing because I trust in Him, no matter how ugly it may seem."

The very next day, I attended a local women's leadership conference. I asked my boss a few weeks in advance if he would allow me to use work time to attend and he said, "No. It's a personal conference." I disagreed, was disappointed (to say the least) and wanted to eat my feelings after that conversation. Instead, I practiced Urge Surfing. Think of Urge Surfing as "riding the waves" of emotions without going to do what naturally comes to mind (for me, I wanted to stuff my feelings with food). It was a long ride of Urge Surfing – distracting myself from bingeing and simply allowing myself to feel the feelings. Doing this alternate activity (Urge Surfing) allowed my urge to binge calm down, and I moved on by telling myself that I was still going to attend the conference and would enjoy it just as much. I took a personal vacation day and spent the day on myself. I was so thankful I did that. In the past, I would not have thought of taking the day to myself and putting myself out there.

While at the conference, I introduced myself to a few of the speakers, including the co-founder of the Team Women organization. Pam Borton was the former women's basketball coach for the University of Minnesota before she launched her own coaching and consulting business, and the non-profit organization hosting the event, Team Women. Surprising myself, I showed up with confidence enough to introduce myself to Pam. She won't remember me, yet I will remember how I showed up for that brief introduction.

Also, I didn't know anyone else who was attending the conference (my good friend, Karen, was planning on attending with me, yet her plans changed when she intended to relocate to Florida in June), so I sat at a table of about five other women who I did not know. We exchanged stories, and I could not believe I was showing up like I was. It was a wonderful conference and we heard from some wonderful speakers. As I left the event for the day, I reflected on what I noticed from each of the key-note speakers: they were all comfortable sharing their journey and story because they knew and believed they would not be who they are today without those hiccups or struggles. They also knew the struggles were not who they were. Profound!

About six weeks after this event, when I was feeling fairly confident, a picture of myself pulled me back a bit, reminding me that recovery is a winding journey. It was June 1, and I had two graduation parties to attend that day.

When I got to the first one, it was for the daughter of a former associate of mine, Christin. I had left the company and that team a little over four years prior. There were team members at the party who I had not seen since I left. My friend, the host, decided it would be a good idea to take a photo of us four former team members at the party. I didn't think anything of it. I spent time socializing with my former co-workers and their families before we left to head to the next party. It felt like a reunion of sorts; like old times with good people.

The next party was for my good friend Karen's son. This would be the last hurrah for them before they officially moved to Florida in late June. I enjoyed Karen's son's party, and then went home.

Later that evening as I was getting ready for bed, I looked at my phone and saw the text from Christin. "Thanks again for being there. Love and hugs to you," she texted along with the picture. "You're welcome. Of course I think that's not a good picture of me," I text back. She responded, "Please know what a beautiful person you are, how much you mean to me and what a difference you have made in my life. Hugs and love to you." I respond back, knowing I need compassion in this moment, with, "Thank you sooooo much. Your words mean so much to me. And I know. I gotta work on loving myself no matter what I look like. Thanks for being someone who loves her friends unconditionally. You are one special person. I'm so honored to call you a friend and be invited to spend time with you and your family and friends today."

I would process that moment in my journal the next morning:

> "I am going to need _EXTREME_ self-compassion today. And now, the tears start. The music in my ears brings tears to my eyes. I release all the pain and suffering I feel right now, in this moment. I want to accept and love my body just as it is. And right now, it is hard. I got the photo Christin took at her daughter's grad party. She sent it right before I went to bed. And Ed came out and attacked and shamed. I thought I looked good yesterday, until I saw pictures of myself. I looked so big. And yet, the silver lining is that I had a _HUGE_ smile on my face. It reflected how good I felt and how good I feel inside.

Why is loving myself unconditionally so hard? I can't be conditional with my self-love and compassion and expect to move forward and recover. F*ck you, Ed. I hate you, the disease. You have made me feel so invalid for so f*cking long. I need you to leave my life NOW. You are not worthy of my time or energy. You love it when you get a f*cking grip on me like that. You think you are in the driver's seat and you are not. I run the show here and I get to decide the next move. I will not choose to give into you. I deserve so much more than you. You are a f*cking a**hole.

I'm so much better than you and all your sneaky little tricks. I'm not getting the big gulp at the gas station after church today. That's you. You get so much pleasure from me drinking that. You love to be in control when that happens. And I'm not giving you that today. I got you. You are the f*cking one who has messed with me for too many years. And I'm the one who's laughing because I got three really good friends out of my desire to rid myself of you. You are the one who causes me to doubt myself, to bash myself, to say "if only…then I can." That's you. I'm breaking up with you. I'm taking care of myself in a healthy way going forward."

The following week, I would start the next phase of my coach training. In this phase, we would go deeper on the concepts, lead a group coaching session and have real one-on-one coaching sessions with our classmates. I was in heaven! I was where I was meant to be. There was no doubt this profession would be my next career move. All the progress I was making gave me a sense of pride, especially as it related to my perfectionism and following my passions. I captured this in my journal the evening of our first class:

"I'm <u>uber</u> proud of myself! I didn't over-prepare for my group coaching session tonight and I rocked it. I let things go and just had fun with things. I asked for help from Ruth (my trainer) as needed when I wanted validation of my approach at the beginning. I didn't let any of the feedback get to me. I rocked it and I feel so validated that I am on the right path with the coaching stuff. I do really want to pursue this, even if it's on the side and one or two clients at a time. I've enjoyed it. It's been a fun ride. I have

six more weeks, and also have to do three, 60-minute coaching sessions with someone and be a client for them too."

Just as I finished up my coach training in mid-July, my family and my sister Missy's family headed up to Nisswa for a family vacation in a home on a lake. It was so much fun. We stayed at the same resort on Middle Cullen Lake that we did the previous year, yet this time we stayed in a bigger home and spent three nights there instead. We had a great time.

Even though we had fun at the cabin with my family and Missy's, there were times when I caught myself comparing my body to my sister's. She had lost a lot of weight and was not using food to comfort. Rather than focus on the gifts I had in my life and my own recovery, my eating disorder chose to focus on the comparison of bodies, which triggered a pang of envy here and there as noted in my journal one night:

> *"She (my sister) just looks like she's in a good spot. And she prioritizes her health. She eats small meals and ensures to get in a balance of foods. She takes care of herself. She took a bath as she needed them and went on walks too. She has such determination to not go back to her old self. She looks so at peace. And that's a place I want to get to. She really does seem to be enjoying her life now. Food used to comfort her too. Now it is used for true hunger."*

Thankfully I would have an appointment with my dietitian, Katherine, after returning from vacation. I always felt more focused on my own journey and recovery after seeing her. Only after seeing her did I realize how much my eating disorder was being triggered at the moment, as captured in my journal the day after my appointment:

> *"I went to my dietitian appointment with Katherine yesterday. And it was probably a good thing. I didn't realize how much seeing my sister eat and be thin would trigger my eating disorder so much. I thought it was just me who couldn't handle it, but Ed took over and took advantage of the situation.*
>
> *Katherine reminded me that I have an eating disorder. She also reminded me that my sister was not diagnosed with an eating*

disorder. She doesn't have a distorted relationship with food, but I do. I have a f*cking eating disorder and I didn't ask for it or deserve it. It helped me cope with all my anxiety and empty feelings of love. It really helped me, but it no longer helps me now.

I didn't realize how much I was impacted by my eating disorder on vacation until I processed everything with Katherine. She reminded me I have an eating disorder and that going back to the basics is a good idea. I'm going to track my food and emotions in the Recovery app, be mindful of portion sizes and monitor my hunger and fullness cues."

Journaling about this situation really allowed me to see the behavioral chain that was happening. A behavioral chain (analysis) is another way of saying you can see all the factors that led up to a problem behavior. In the case of my vacation story with my sister, seeing firsthand how my sister took care of herself, was at peace with her life, ate small meals, etc., (factors) triggered me to compare our bodies and to eat for comfort (behavior).

About this same time, I started seeing a new therapist at The Emily Program, as Nicole had left. I started seeing Kris that July, and she was (is) awesome. She specializes in EMDR and parts of self-work, which we dove into immediately. I was telling her about my experiences on vacation and my triggers. She said how the body image issues I was having on the beach on vacation were probably from when I was younger. I told her how I immediately thought of my 5th grade track event at Sheridan Elementary. I was wearing my pink terry-cloth matching shorts and shirt set and had pig-tails in my hair. As I mentioned in previous chapters, this is when the boys called me "Tick Tock Titty." I felt so humiliated at the time. These were classmates and boys I had a crush on. I felt ashamed of my body because I felt too big and was blossoming out in more than one area of my body.

I had no idea that this is what came to mind when I was at the beach a few weeks before, comparing myself to others. A realization started: many of my issues stem from younger parts of myself. Further into the practice, the predominant parts that would come forward in our EMDR work together would be my seven-year-old self who didn't feel worthy of her dad's love, my 13-year-old self who wanted to be perfect so mom had one less thing to worry about and avoid adding more conflict into the family, and my 20-year-old self who wanted to exceed and accelerate at everything to gain the approval of my dad and others to feel worthy.

During the summer of 2019, Leanne, Stefania, Kathryn and I started to plan monthly brunch dates on Saturdays at the Key's Cafe in Woodbury. It was so fun to meet up with them in person, since we had all graduated from the DBT program by now. Since we didn't have that weekly DBT session anymore, the monthly gathering would have to do. We continued these until March 2020, when we were hit with a global pandemic. I miss those monthly brunches.

One time, only Leanne and I were able to make it. The two of us talked for five straight hours! I was starting to get hungry again just as we were leaving! My husband asked me what I could possibly talk to someone about for five straight hours, so of course I reminded him that girls can talk about lots of things when you have so much in common!

The summer of 2019 ended quickly, as they usually do, and Kaitlyn would head back to Mankato for her third year of college in late August. Unlike her first year of college when I was suffering from major depression and in the middle of my eating disorder, the goodbye was not as bad, as I noted in my journal:

> *"I teared up a little when I first started driving to Mankato with Kaitlyn, as she said her favorite part of the 15 weeks she was home for the summer was family time. I teared up when I hugged her goodbye too.*
>
> *I know it will be good for her to be away again. She will continue to mature and grow. It's always amazing to sit back and watch your kiddos. They are both amazing kids. I'm going to miss her, and yet I'm really excited for her. She's a beautiful soul. And I'm so lucky to be her mom. Lucky."*

Soon, it was time for Dale and I to take our much-anticipated trip to Arizona. I was really looking forward to all the extra time we would spend together from Wednesday until Sunday on this trip. We'd planned it back in

May. Neither of our kids had any interest in going with us, so we planned it around a time when Ian had an extended period off from school for teacher workshops so he could (once again) stay home and take care of Ollie. This was becoming a habit of ours!

The day before we left for Arizona was the 13th anniversary of my dad's passing. Usually this time of year brings forward thoughts about dying young or enjoying retirement or living life to the fullest or missing my dad altogether. And sometimes it is a mix of it all. This year was no different.

I caught myself comparing myself to others – people I know and people I only know by social media, Ted Talks, or a book they wrote. As I journaled that night, I felt like I wanted to go back and do life over again or at least to a time when my kids were little. Then, I wanted to be like someone else who wrote a book about navigating midlife and menopause. I went all over the place. Then, I finally became more mindful and wrote this:

> *"I want to prioritize my mental and physical health. No more chasing. No more looking for someone's approval. Just my own mental and physical well-being. It's hard. I want to chase after what others have. And yet, I've got an awesome life right in front of me. It's the best life for me. And it's my life. I want to live rather than drool over others' lives on Facebook and Instagram. It's not worth my mental health. I want to live my life just as God meant it to be – good, bad, ugly, excellent, and everything in between."*

We boarded our flight super early the next morning – our flight left at 6:05 a.m. We arrived 30 minutes earlier than anticipated in Arizona, so it was around 9:00 a.m. Minnesota time (7:00 a.m. Arizona time) by now. I was tired already. And a bit hungry. Within an hour of landing, we headed toward the National Petrified Forest from the airport after stopping at the restrooms, getting our luggage and picking up our rental car. Dale had mapped it all out and planned for us to stop in a little town along the way called Payson to grab lunch/brunch and shop for some snacks and water for the rest of our trip at the local Walmart. He was always very planful about our itinerary on trips. Our deal was that I would book the airfare and hotel, and he would do the rest. This trip was no different.

Nearly three hours after landing in Phoenix, we pulled into the parking lot of a mom-and-pop diner called the Beeline Cafe. It was a cute little place that only accepted cash. Good thing we had some cash on us and the meals were not that expensive (we typically use our credit card, and then pay it off in full when the bill comes). Neither of us carry much cash at any given time. I was beyond hungry at this point, so much so that I ate my meal in like five minutes or less. For whatever reason, I didn't ask Dale to pull over along the way so I could get the lunch I'd packed in my carry-on bag. It was my eating disorder's way of playing mind games with me I guess. Well after our trip was over, I would realize that this trip would have many instances of eating disorder behavior. Because I was in the presence of my husband 24/7, my eating disorder did not like that I couldn't eat in secret.

The rest of our day was jammed full of stopping to smell the roses along the way to the Petrified Forest, driving through the forest, stopping in Winslow, AZ, and then on toward Sedona. I would occasionally reach over and tell Dale that I loved him as I touched his arm ever so tenderly. He would respond with deep love and compassion too. It was pure heaven to be in the presence of my husband, my soul mate, with uninterrupted attention. It fell in line with my love language of quality time, that's for sure!

On our second day in Arizona, we found a great place for breakfast in Sedona with 101 different omelet options! (For anyone who may want to go there to pick from 101 variations of omelets while in Sedona, it's called The Coffee Pot.) There were so many choices on the menu that day, and I tried to listen to what my body told me it needed in that moment. Because it was a bit chilly on their outdoor patio, I ordered a hot chocolate and the #26 omelet - sausage, bacon, tomato and cheese. It was so nice to sit with Dale and plan out our day. This would be our only full day in Sedona, so we wanted to get in some hiking in the red rocks, along with seeing the chapel in the rocks (Chapel of the Holy Cross).

We had a lovely start to our day. We went back to our hotel room after eating breakfast to pack up our things for a day of adventure. We went up to the Chamber of Commerce to ask about all the hiking available in the area. She showed us all the trails on a map, explaining which ones were of which hiking ability. I didn't think anything of the trails that were marked as "easy." I even thought I was up for the ones marked "intermediate." Boy, was I in for a rude awakening!

Our adventure started by going to the Chapel of the Holy Cross. Thankfully, that was our first stop, as things got so crowded as we were leaving. It was breathtaking to take in the calm of that chapel. I sat down in a pew and said some prayers. Others were doing the same. I only wish I could go to mass in a beautiful place like that every week. Just a unique experience for sure. There was really no hiking at this stop, other than the hike up the slope of the parking lot to the actual structure. This would turn out to be the easiest "hike" in Sedona.

Next, we headed over toward the Bell Rock Trail. By the looks of the map, it was a more advanced hike than either of us could endure, so we decided we would start off on another nearby trail that led to a small red rock platform, overlooking the valley below. It was flat going into the hike. I felt at ease with my first few steps. Then, with the first incline nearly 100 feet in, my asthma started to kick in. Wheezing more and more with each step, unfortunately, my eating disorder immediately started to shame me. We were maybe five minutes from the parking lot by this point.

The Ed voice said the nastiest things. "If you weren't so fat and out of shape, you would not have this problem." "If you'd just lose weight, you wouldn't breathe like it's your last breath." "If only you would have kept off the weight over the years." With each step, the voice got louder and louder. "You are no good. You cannot even keep up with your husband. He can't even enjoy himself because of you."

Tears started, then the snot. I bit my lip to hold them back. I had no tissues with me to wipe my nose, so I sucked it back in. At this point, Dale stopped and asked what was wrong. I lied and said, "Nothing." With that, my eating disorder said loudly, "You are no good. You are holding your husband back." I bit my lip harder, and then said to my husband, "My asthma is bothering me today." He asked if I wanted to take a break. My eating disorder replied, "No, I'll be okay," as I bit my lip even harder to stop the tears. We walked on.

As we rounded the corner and inclined up even more, my breath became more labored, in addition to the Ed voice weighing heavily, being full-blown obnoxious by now. I couldn't take another step. The Ed voice in my head made me freeze. Dale asked what was wrong again. The tears just flooded from my eyes at that moment. It was like the tears were a wash that signaled I needed to let go, to be vulnerable, to come "clean" as to what was going on. Dale gently nudged my arm and said ever so lovingly, "Let's pull over to the side here and let others pass us." Then, he looked me in the eyes and asked, "What's wrong?" I so didn't want to tell him what was really going on. I was so ashamed.

I was beyond compassion for myself at that point, yet courage showed up for me in that moment. "My asthma is really bothering me and making it hard for me to breathe. On top of that, my eating disorder is telling me that it wouldn't be like this if I wasn't so fat." The tears just flowed. Dale hugged me close and kissed my head ever so tenderly. I shook as the tears flowed. I continued through tears and snot, "I am so fat and out of shape that I feel like I really let you down. You want to climb up to the top of that platform, and I can't take another step. I am holding you back. I feel less than, like you deserve so much more."

Dale lovingly responded, "You are not holding me back. You are all I ever needed. And if I'm honest, I am a little winded climbing this too. Let's sit down for a bit, and then we can head back down." I cried as he held me close and kissed my head tenderly like a mom kisses a young child who has been wounded from falling off a bike. It was as if I was being vulnerable with him for the very first time. Up to this point, I mostly hid my true feelings from him. I didn't want to be "too much drama" for him. He was a simple guy.

Yet, my therapist, Kris, had been suggesting to me since we started working together that I needed to be more vulnerable with him. I always thought I was…until this moment. Before, I had kept a lot from him, not truly sharing much about how my eating disorder had and was impacting me. I thought he'd leave me if he knew what was really happening – if he knew I still occasionally ate large amounts of food in secret to comfort myself. That I had a voice inside my head telling me I was no good. All along, I feared he would leave me if I told him what was really going on with my eating disorder. Yet, I showed up in the moment and let my authentic voice lead the conversation that day.

I went on to tell him what was really going on inside my head: all the shame and Ed comments. At one point, I told him, "The mental part is much harder than the physical part of the asthma being triggered." After a long, nearly 15 minutes of spilling my heart out about what had been happening, and then receiving a lot of loving compassion from Dale, I told him to climb to the top of the platform without me. "I will wait here for you to return." He insisted that he should stay with me. After a lot of debate back and forth, I finally convinced him to go on.

As I stood in the middle of the open space, waiting for Dale to return, I immediately texted Leanne, Stefania and Kathryn (dubbed my "Emily friends"). "Okay ladies. I'm texting in the middle of a hike with Dale in Sedona. I melted down and sent him on. Having an eating disorder really sucks. My mental and physical state was way off. I couldn't keep going. I think the mental part was worse." They responded instantly, almost all at once. "Dear one be gentle with yourself," said Stefania. Then, Leanne: "Having an eating disorder absolutely sucks! Where are you now? I'm sending you a virtual hug." Then, Kathryn: "Take a deep breath, he will understand. Maybe do like a pro and con. Figure out what triggered it." Then I replied, "Thank you so much ladies. I just need a life line. This is tough. Each step I took, my Ed reminded me how out of shape I am. It's hard." Leanne responded with a bunch of hearts and, "We are here for you!"

I captured a few photos of Dale at the top of that platform, and he did the same as he stood on top. He returned not long before he left – maybe 20 minutes later – and we ventured back to the car. On the path back down, I saw a dead plant with two heads and immediately thought of my eating disorder and its two heads! Oh, how it reared its ugly head at that time!

After the hike, we went to the town of Sedona to find something for lunch, as my breakfast was wearing off and I did not pack a snack. I was still quasi living with an active eating disorder. My eating disorder had convinced me that since I had eaten a hearty omelet breakfast, I did not need to pack a snack to eat before lunch. This is so far from the truth and where the restrictive part of my eating disorder was getting in the way. At my intake appointment, I remember being asked if I ever restricted myself from eating, and firmly replied from my Eating Disorder voice, "No. Would I be at this size if I restricted food?" Yet, I did restrict. And this was one of those moments. A hearty breakfast meant you will need to restrict until lunch, even if you are getting in more movement than usual and your stomach is growling because it is honestly hungry. I am so glad I started eating intuitively shortly after this trip and have had no regrets since.

Because I knew I was hungry and needed something that felt nourishing, I ordered the steak fajitas from the menu at the Bar & Grill. We sat outside and got to look at the red rock formation shaped like a lying down Snoopy in the distance. I ate ever so mindfully. I even ordered a Coke as it sounded good. I drank that mindfully too. I felt so good in that moment – eating nourishing food, out in the open and silencing my eating disorder voice with each bite.

We shopped around town before heading over to Doe Mountain. I was determined to give this hike a try. I was fully nourished and feeling good about my mental state. We were about two hours from sunset when we started to hike that formation. A lot of steps were built into the paths; lots of winding trails, and then more steps. We were maybe 30 minutes into this hike when my asthma kicked in. Instead of melting down like I had earlier, I gently turned to Dale and told him I was not able to continue on. Insisting he should go on without me, he responded to me that we would both go back this time together.

Back at our car, it was about an hour from when we first ventured off. By now, it was about 60 minutes until sunset. Knowing how long it took us to go the little distance we did, we were both thankful we did not continue on. We may have been able to reach the mountain top before sunset (perhaps), yet we would have been walking back down in the dark. This would have been totally unsafe!

As the saying goes, things happen for a reason. And in this case, it meant we would return home to Minnesota safely without killing ourselves navigating steep declines in the dark!

· 14 ·

Radical Acceptance Comes During a Worldwide Pandemic

"Sometimes, you just gotta jump off the cliff anyway."
—*Jen Nelson, LPCC*

 **For years**, my job mindset struggled, always thinking I was unsatisfied. It wasn't until 2020 when a worldwide pandemic happened when I would finally radically accept what was at the time, knowing I had my eyes on the long-term prize: the most fulfilling career was coming.

I finished the first phase of my coach training in the summer of 2018. I fell in love with all of it. *This is what I was meant to be after all these years* I would tell myself. Coaching combined my desire to help people (the social worker in me) and my 22+ years of experience in Corporate America. Maybe in some ways it finally combined what my name stood for as well. My mom always told me they named me Teresa Joan for a reason. Teresa meant "little flower," and Joan was for the strength like Joan of Arc. This little flower, who has strength like Joan of Arc, likes to help people. Bottom line: coaching people *is* helping people. It may not be the social worker that I once desired to be way back in college, but this is who I was meant to be. Everything leading up to this moment was necessary. It all needed to be part of my journey to get me to this destination.

My second portion of coach training was in the summer of 2019. This was after I had spent a year in weekly DBT sessions, becoming more effective and assertive in my communication and increasing my own confidence. I was slowly peeling back all the layers of hurt and becoming that little flower I was always meant to be. I watered her. I nurtured her. She was slowly blooming like she was always meant to.

By this time, I was coaching people on the side and really enjoying it. There was nothing better than sitting down one-on-one with someone and listening to their story, learning how they want to move forward in life and what their hopes and dreams are. Creating this safe space for them to dream, and then see those dreams come true was incredibly fulfilling for me.

In addition to the coaching I was doing on the side, I was still working in IT in Corporate America. During this time, I would still get upset about things that happened at my "day job" and let it spiral out of control. It was like I was picking at a scab that would not go away. Pick. Pick. Pick. Slowly, it would start to bleed. I'd stop, the blood would dry, only long enough until the next incident of fear and anxiety started running the show. Someone would say something I didn't like or my boss would provide me feedback that I'd take personally, and I'd slowly close the flower that had been blooming ever so beautifully just moments before. I had not yet radically accepted *this is how things are, for the time being. This won't last forever.* Funny how I was not coaching myself with these words like I would coach my own clients. Somehow what was helpful for them, didn't fall on my own ears in these moments of anxiety, fear and frustration.

Then, a pandemic happened in March of 2020. Dale and I had just returned from a spring break vacation in the Punta Cana region of the Dominican Republic. When we left, COVID-19 had just hit Minnesota, and New York and Seattle were hot spots already. We only had two cases in our area when we left. It was no big deal at the time. We enjoyed five out of the six days we were on the island. By the time the last day rolled around, we started to worry that our flight home would be cancelled and we'd be stuck there (even though it was paradise there, being away from home during a major outbreak of a virus that was killing people felt reckless and worrisome).

While I was gone in paradise, my employer mandated work-from-home policies for everyone, as would most other companies around the states, and for that matter, the world. This was hard for me. We returned home from paradise to stores with no toilet paper or meat on their shelves. No peanut butter, pasta, or canned foods either. People had been panic-buying while we were in paradise. Kaitlyn texted us while we were gone, asking if she should go buy toilet paper and food. *No way*, we thought. That is, until she shared pictures of empty shelves from our local grocery store when she did venture out.

I did my own panic shopping just hours after we arrived home. I bought food like I'd never see it on the shelves again. I would buy the last three packages of chicken breasts they had on their shelves. I would buy the last boxes of pasta they had on their shelves, not considering other people after me who also needed to provide food on their tables for their families. Part of this was eating disorder related, while part of this was pure anxiety-driven fear.

The next day, I returned back to work...remotely of course. I kicked, screamed and threw every fit I could on every person I could about working from home. *I can't do this*, is what my anxiety fed to me. I would complain to anyone who would listen. A few of my therapy appointments had to be cancelled, until they set up tele-health capabilities. In those first few days after returning, I probably needed a combination of therapy and my own wise mind more than anything. I needed a gentle reminder that I can do anything I put my mind to and this was only temporary. There had been other challenges I had overcome in the past, and soon, this would be one too. I needed my own wise mind to remind me of this, and yet because I was not radically accepting anything at the moment, I couldn't see a way forward.

Before I headed to paradise, I found out my dietitian, Katherine, who had been working with me for the majority of my journey, would be leaving The Emily Program to pursue an advanced degree to become a physician's assistant. She told me she wanted to help change the culture of the medical world and help those with eating disorders feel like they had a safe space to come. They did not need to spend time only talking about changing the number on the scale.

Before the pandemic happened, her last day was going to be at the end of

March. This meant that my appointment with her after vacation was going to be my last. I was happy to hear that she had pushed out her last day by two weeks due to the pandemic, so I would get to see her one last time in mid-April before having to say goodbye. I was so incredibly thankful for all she helped me accomplish. She helped me overcome the power and control cake had over me. I was well on my way with soda pop too. I was going to miss her...a lot. Countless hours had been spent together. It was almost like she knew me more than some of my good friends. She definitely knew me more than some of my own relatives.

When sharing with Katherine about my grocery shopping experience and feeling like I needed to purchase a ton more food than I needed, she invited me to journal after our appointment about how Ed's story of "not enough" was coming up in my daily routine. This was powerful. I was also feeling "not good enough" when it came to productivity at work. I was working remotely and trying to adjust to a new way of working, which meant I was not quite as productive as before. Ed took advantage of these moments. He snuck in and led me to believe I was not good enough if I didn't work at least eight full hours during the day. Ed did not allow for any mental or physical breaks. He told me I wasn't good enough unless I excelled at my job. In his eyes, it was not okay to take my mind off things by doing a puzzle or taking a walk for 20 minutes. *This is hard stuff to handle, yet you're not good enough unless you are fully productive.* Lies. Lies.

After talking with Katherine, I would take advantage of a good journal session later that evening:

> *"I just realized that Ed's coming up when I worry I didn't 'do' enough while working at home. If I keep focused on what I didn't do, I won't have time to celebrate what I <u>did</u> do. If I keep tabs on the hours I spend 'doing' at work, it won't add up to eight hours. I'm supposed to work eight hours is what Ed says. Anything short of that isn't good enough. Gosh. I feel so bashed by Ed already. No wonder why I feel so drained after work. I'm constantly fending off Ed and trying to convince myself that I am enough. That is hard work. I can only take so much. It's no wonder I'm exhausted most days. That's a lot of energy to convince yourself you are good enough and you are doing a good job. Imagine how much more*

relaxed and actually productive you'd feel if you let those thoughts go. If you gave them little energy, you would have more energy to take into your spare time at home.

I really do want to be my biggest cheerleader. I want to show up for myself. I want to be my own best friend. What would happen if you kept cheering for yourself? What would be possible? I can and will be my best friend and biggest cheerleader. I will root for me and do some fact checking when Ed starts to say it's not good enough. No one is 100% productive for all eight hours . . . I have healthy boundaries. I have passions outside of work. Work is where I spend a lot of time during the work week, and it does not define me. It's a job and I will keep reminding myself of that."

Two weeks after coming home from paradise and the day after seeing Katherine, I had my first remote therapy session with Kris. Kris was good. We had been working together for eight months on peeling back the layers to determine where the "never good enough" was coming from. We were completing EMDR therapy while in her office over these eight months. We would not be able to complete it in person now, and yet working with Kris for eight months every week had allowed me to make tremendous progress in healing my old wounds and understanding which parts of myself were showing up on any given day. This was powerful for me in my recovery. It meant I understood *who* was showing up in certain circumstances and *why* they were showing up. Understanding has a powerful way to connect you to the actions you need to take to move forward. Understanding heals the soul.

In this particular session with Kris, we discussed how my parts of self (Kris' type of therapy is based on the Internal Family Systems therapy approach) really need me to show them that I am here for them, that I'm CEO of me and I can validate their feelings and choose good things for them. The inner parts of me have seen someone else run the show for so long, they may not trust me. If I keep showing up compassionately, I'll make progress. A few days after this session, guilt (Ed) started to wash over me for choosing to journal and take care of my needs first before dropping my mom's birthday card off. I journaled about how my core self wants to feel and show up instead:

"My core self wants to be 100% authentic. My core self wants to do what feels right for me regardless of what's going on for others. My core self wants to let all my parts of self know that we will be okay. That I can lead us just like I've led others. We don't need someone's permission to be authentic and do things our way. I will lead you all from my core. We don't need food or pop to cope. We've got a full menu of healthy coping skills. And Ed, I know you've had to protect me for years from hurt. And I commend you for doing that. You did what you thought was best for me at the time. You protected me from hurt and shame. You wanted so badly to protect me. And I am thankful for that. I want you to know I appreciate it and that I am here to lead us to recovery. I am smart. I can be authentic and lead us to the healthy path. You can help encourage us to do that by gently reminding me of what's important. And reminding me to be gentle with myself and offer extreme self-compassion. Likewise, I am going to offer all parts extreme compassion. There is no good in shame. God has gifted my core with beauty and He wants that to show time and time again.

The part of self that comes up is my little 7-year-old self. She wants me to love myself and make hard choices so I can honor myself. The Ed part wanted to go to Mom's to drop off a card for her birthday. He started to say 'You should…' My 7-year-old self says, 'But you planned to do this journaling and spend time taking care of yourself. I want you to give that nurturing to me please. Please prioritize yourself. You called your mom and can drop off her card when she least expects it. Your plan for tonight was to do just this. I am happy you are taking care of yourself.'

This feels BIG. I mean I am doing something I wanted to do and am prioritizing my needs. I didn't want to keep avoiding this activity. I am honoring my needs and my feelings. I can't control how my mom will feel about this. Only she is in charge of her emotions. Not going does not mean I don't love her. I do love her. I happened to prioritize my needs. It was overdue. I want to keep doing this. I want to keep honoring my true authentic feelings, wants and needs."

Feeding My Soul

"Joy can be achieved."
—*Jen Nelson, LPCC*

 **As the** pandemic of 2020 moved forward, and it appeared as though there was no end in sight, I began to start living my life without holding back. While it took a while for me to adjust to the working from home thing for my 9 to 5 job, I felt like I finally had some space to really start dreaming during my non-working hours. I didn't have a stressful commute to add to my day anymore. I didn't have a calendar filled with commitments before and after work and on the weekend. I could prep our dinner at 3:00 in the afternoon if it was needed. I was walking during the day more than ever before (my pooch was loving this, by the way). I was sleeping better. I was writing more (thus the start of this book that had always been only a "someday" dream). I had vivid dreams and long, deep conversations with good friends (over Zoom and the phone of course).

When restrictions started to lift in early April, I had a socially distanced coffee with my good friend Leanne in the parking lot of Starbuck's, as she happened to be in my neighborhood due to work. Later that month, Stefania, Leanne, Kathryn and I would have a socially distanced gathering in a nearby park. It was so good to see them, even if we couldn't hug each other.

While others were having a hard time coping, I felt guilty, as it seemed like I was in my element. It's like the stressful life I was living pre-Covid had made me numb from truly living and the lifestyle that Covid was giving me (i.e., staying at home and just enjoying life and the little things) was like the doctor's orders I had needed for years. It had finally clicked. I didn't need to lose weight to be happy; I just needed to listen to what my mind, body and soul needed each and every day, and then go do it.

Around this same time, I hired my own coach (again). I was seeing great progress in my eating disorder recovery and felt I was ready to put my goals into action. Someone needed to help me sort that out and give me added accountability.

For some time, it had been nagging me to launch an online presence for my coaching practice. I did not have a website, nor any social media accounts tied to my business. I also wanted to write and share my story more. "Someday" I had wanted to write and publish a book, yet was waiting for the "perfect" story to write. I was a little apprehensive about sharing my own eating disorder recovery story, yet something kept nudging me to do so. Through the help of my coach, I started identifying what I wanted to accomplish, and then the steps it would take to get there. I prioritized and re-prioritized while working with my coach after realizing that some things took longer to implement than I had planned. It felt like I was letting go of something; something I was holding on to for dear life for some reason. It's like I wanted to stay stuck in the past.

Yet, as soon as I started letting my old self go and seeing all the gifts that I was being given in recovery and the pandemic, it's like my best self came forward. I was on fire, and there was no stopping me. Opportunities flooded in. My long-term coaching plans were coming together more and more, as I now had an opportunity to partner with the instructor from my coach training program and several other coaches to offer a group coaching program. The program centered on managing stress and building resilience during unprecedented times. We offered sessions over five weeks and had great feedback on how well these sessions were received. People needed what we were offering. We offered another program that kicked off in early 2021.

I started writing this book at the beginning of May 2020 as one of the many goals I had wanted to accomplish while working with my coach. I launched my website and my Instagram account tied to my business the next month

(June). I wrote weekly blogs at the beginning, and it seemed so natural for me. In October, my Instagram site became my "blogging" of sorts.

In May, I was also put in touch with Angie at The Emily Program who produces the *Peace Meal* podcast for them. After finding much courage and knowing that my story may help at least one other middle-aged woman out there, I agreed to share my own recovery story for the *Peace Meal* podcast. We recorded it in July, and it was published on August 31. All these gifts…

As I was saying yes to the gifts that were before me, I knew there was something holding me back from fully embracing them. I had failed to share my own eating disorder diagnosis with my best friend, Heather. We had been friends since the 7th grade when we sat next to each other in our homeroom class. We were still friends after all these years – through all the ups and downs of life, and despite living in different states for the past 25 years. Yet, I had not told Heather about my eating disorder because I felt ashamed for having it. And now that I was going to publicly share my story and was no longer ashamed, I did not want her to find out by stumbling upon the podcast herself. I would send her the following text on May 27:

> *"Hi there. Thinking of you. Wanted to ask if you have a free and quiet 30 minutes to connect in the next week or so. I want to confide in you about something that's really hard for me to share. No need to be alarmed. I just want to share, as I've been keeping it inside for a very long time, waiting for the most perfect time. And the longer I hold off, the harder it gets. Hope you are doing okay."*

She responded about 35 minutes later and said, "Hi. Just saw this. Yes of course, anytime is good, anytime you need me, never hesitate to call."

I knew this was going to be hard, and my eating disorder tried hard to prevent me from having the conversation. I replied, "It's late for you (she is an hour ahead of my time zone) so we can do another night if you prefer." She responded immediately, "Now is good, seriously," so I called her after I went into my master bathroom and gave myself a pep talk in the mirror. As soon as she answered, I cried. It's like my eating disorder wanted me to be so ashamed. I kept going and told her all about my eating disorder diagnosis, my recovery and where I was at the moment. I also shared about being on an upcoming podcast, sharing my story. She was so loving and compassionate and supportive. I couldn't believe I had kept all of this part of me from her, yet I was being given this gift to ask for forgiveness and her acceptance of me.

In early July, I enrolled in another coaching program that was being offered to certain coaches. I jumped on the opportunity (lover of learning is one of my key character strengths) and was so glad I did. It introduced me to a phenomenal leader, Shirzad Charmine, the founder of POSITIVE INTELLIGENCE®, and his famous PQ program. This became a game-changer for me. We spent six weeks learning about our own inner judge and the accomplice saboteurs, along with our inner sage and its powers. I'd been a meditator for over three years by this point and thought I had a good handle on my positivity. It wasn't until we practiced PQ reps (little spurts of mindfulness) in the middle of the moment when I realized how I was only practicing mindfulness at 5:30 in the morning when no real stressors had hit me yet for the day.

I learned to quiet my mind and be focused on the present. It showed me how the strengths of my pleaser were being taken too far, and I was making decisions based on pleasing others. I also learned how critical my inner judge was being, mostly being critical of myself and my body. One day, we practiced an exercise with a picture of our younger selves. This offered such tremendous insight into why I was having such struggles accepting myself. It was such a huge gift for me.

As I moved my body daily, surrounded myself with good people, gave myself plenty of rest and downtime, did things I enjoyed, and started practicing more empathy toward myself, I realized all the gifts I was given by having an eating disorder. If I didn't have an eating disorder, chances are that I would not have found the courage to pursue my coaching, writing and speaking dreams. I would be waiting for the day when I had lost enough weight to make that happen. I would not have met three wonderful ladies who I am blessed to call friends. My relationship with Dale would not have improved, nor would my relationship with food or my body. I would still be searching for my worth in my title, my salary, my body size, my bank account. I was well on my way toward full recovery, all because I decided that I was worth so much more.

· 16 ·

A Recovered Life

"How freeing would it be to lean into discomfort and acceptance, rather than to think life will never have discomfort?"
—Jen Nelson, LPCC

 **The day** came when I would finally declare myself "recovered" in October 2020, almost three years to the date of my diagnosis. I had been feeling like I had been truly recovered for several months, yet was afraid to *fully* declare my freedom. The hyper-vigilant part of self (my 13-year-old self) was nagging me that there may be danger lurking around the corner; that there may be another trigger within a matter of days to set me back to square one. But the day I declared my recovered status, I felt free.

All the noise left; the eating disorder was quieted in that instant. It was like *not* declaring my recovered status kept me in active eating disorder mode, even if ever so slightly. It's like not being in recovered status gave my Ed permission to show up as a coping mechanism "in the event that…" He was holding me back. He wanted me to keep saying I was recovering, as that meant he was still in charge.

I remember the day when I was ready to declare my "recovered" status. It was a Tuesday. I had a bi-weekly therapy appointment with Kris at The Emily Program. It was a virtual session, as we were still in the middle of the global pandemic of Covid at that time. It was October 20 – one week shy of the three-year anniversary of my eating disorder diagnosis. I declared my recovered status, and Kris provided me with a Recovery Relapse plan that I was to complete before my next session in two weeks. Once we reviewed the plan together at my next appointment in two weeks, I was eligible to start seeing Kris once a month.

At this point of my recovery state, I wanted to give Body Image yoga one more try. I had tried it back in the spring of 2018 while at The Emily Program, yet my body was not ready for it, and my eating disorder really fought me at that time. I went to two sessions, and declared it was not for me. Now that I am further removed from the situation, I really think it was my eating disorder hanging on tight rather than authentic me who made that declaration back then.

Kris and I decided that giving Body Image yoga at The Emily Program a try would be a good way for me to set myself up for success in my discharge journey. I also really wanted to be in tune with my body and have a good yoga practice. The following Monday after my appointment with Kris, I started Body Image yoga, which was led by Mary (therapist) and Sarah (yoga instructor). It was done virtually over Zoom just like my appointments had been because of Covid.

That first night, I was nervous. I did not know who else would be attending and was a bit worried about following along from my computer in our den. It turned out, a mixture of age groups were in attendance, which put me at ease. There were a couple young adult women there, along with one woman who was about my age and another woman in her 30's. I realized the age of everyone else really did not matter in this setting. We were not spending time talking about our experiences like we did during IOP or DBT group therapy. While we did state our intentions at the beginning of the session and process for a bit at the end, the whole session was focused on staying on our own mat and having our own experience.

The first night was beautiful. I felt so calm afterwards. It was like my head shut off with all the thinking and my body took charge, led by my heart and soul, so I could really just BE in that moment. It was a wonderful practice. I wondered why I hadn't given it a legitimate try back two years prior. Then, I remembered *why* didn't really matter. What mattered was I was at this point in my journey, and I truly felt recovered.

I continued yoga for 11 additional weeks. Some weeks I was really in tune with my body and was able to move from my head to my heart easily, and other times I was not. But here's the beauty: it all was part of a beautiful practice and didn't matter how "easy" it was. There was no right or wrong way to do yoga, I learned. My body will know what is right, and sometimes that meant being in the fetal position for a bulk of the session. When I got out of my head, my body showed up and took the lead.

When I gave it a try the first time, I don't think I was ready. I was still in my own head and in my own way. If it wasn't perfect, I gave up so easily. This was my eating disorder driving me to give up. "If things don't go perfectly, give up," he would say. I believed him for so long, and I am so glad I have separated myself from him now. I can show up in the messiest of moments and just BE. I can sit with the uncomfortableness and tell myself that *this, too, shall pass.*

In my work world, I am noticing this too. Prior to declaring myself recovered, I would constantly convince myself that if things weren't perfect, I needed to give up and go to the next job. I couldn't take it. Much energy was spent looking for another job. It was going to make me happier I thought, so I was constantly looking whenever I had a bad day at work, something didn't go my way, or if my boss provided me with feedback.

Now, I can easily see how this was all part of my eating disorder and my anxiety feeding on that. I can laugh with my therapist when I tell her how I couldn't wait to leave my company and my boss when I was first starting IOP. "Like I would have had time to focus on recovery and a brand-new company/job back then," I chuckled with Kris. I can laugh about it now, because I realize it was not my authentic self who wanted to run and hide when things weren't going perfectly. It was Ed. And it took me three years of healing and recovering to see that.

I am so glad I stayed at my company and pursued my passions outside of my role at my employer. My employer is a great employer. I have been given opportunities to learn and grow, which has helped me in my coaching practice. Because of my eating disorder, I now have the coaching practice on the side that once was only a dream, saved for a perfect *someday* to launch it.

My goal is to retire from my corporate role in five years and to be completely focused on coaching, speaking and writing. Yet, the most important thing I learned in my recovery journey was that I am not my role at my employer (or my side business), nor the performance rating I receive at the end of each year. I am so much more. I am someone who loves the sun and the beach. I am someone who loves to travel. I am someone who loves to have a deep conversation with someone. I am someone who loves to write. I am someone who loves to walk two to three times a day in mini, 15-minute spurts with my pooch by my side. I am someone who loves to snap a good photo. I am someone who loves to put together a puzzle. I am someone who was meant to be on this planet, helping spread sunshine like the "little flower" my name entails.

*****

If you are suffering from an eating disorder, anxiety, body image issues or unattained dreams, know that you are not alone. This is not your fault at all. It is not because you don't have enough willpower. Most likely, you, too, were taught from an early age that your body needed to be fixed to "fit in" with the "norm." You saw commercials on TV or watched your mom or a close relative diet and comment negatively about her body too. Or worse yet, you saw *all* of these things. Naturally, this led you to think the answer was to change your body. Most likely, you remember the first time someone spoke negatively about your body too – whether that was being teased on the playground by your 5th grade crush like I was, or your own mother or another relative calling you fat, chubby or husky. Somehow, you were led to believe you just weren't enough. To top things off, you may have had an emotionally absent parent who was struggling with their own mental health issues, and you watched them choose unhealthy behaviors as coping mechanisms too. In search for control as an adult, you chose to turn to food, worrying, shaming your body and over-achieving to soothe.

The good news is that there is hope. You *can* overcome an eating disorder and body image issues at any age. You can learn to better manage your anxiety. And once you work on all the inner stuff, you will realize the dreams you once had shelved for *someday* are totally attainable *now*.

To help you on your journey towards your best self yet, here are the top 20 takeaways toward recovery and body acceptance:

1. **Invest in your mental health!** Hire an eating disorder specific therapist and dietitian. They will help you uncover your own trauma and help you heal it, along with treating the eating disorder itself. Ideally, your therapist is also someone able to help you better navigate your anxiety and other mental health related issues. It's okay to get help. Without help, we cannot be there for ourselves or anyone else. We cannot pour from an empty cup!

2. **Practice mindfulness so you can turn down the volume of your inner critic.** To me, this is key to the healing process, body acceptance and full-on freedom. You cannot reach your fullest potential if the volume of your inner critic is on full blast and on repeat throughout the day. You cannot hear the gentle whisper of your soul over the loudness of this critic. I happen to offer a 12-week program that introduces the concept of an inner critic and his cast of characters to begin the process towards freedom and reaching your fullest potential too. I'd love to give you more information about this program at **mybestselfyet.com/1466-2**. The program includes access to a special app for a year, which will help you continue to practice against the inner critic and his cast of characters.

3. **Reject the diet culture around you and practice Intuitive Eating instead, which is NOT another diet, by the way** (don't let anyone on the internet try to convince you otherwise). You cannot recover from food and body image issues if you are continuously chasing after a diet and a desire to change your body. Accept that your body is not a project that needs fixing. This is hard to do yet so freeing when you can! Also, practicing Intuitive Eating will allow you to eat all foods. There's no need to binge on foods (because you are no longer denying yourself the freedom to have the cake and eat it too!).

4. **Surround yourself with a community of support.** It doesn't just take a village to raise a child; it also takes a village to sustain your life. Find people who also believe their body is not the problem. Surround yourself with that love. Take it in and give it out. I lead group coaching circles on self-love now and would love to have you join a circle of unconditional love. You can also join my recently

created private Facebook group (Body Acceptance Group) at this link: **facebook.com/groups/7433577466695957**

5. **Ask yourself, "What do I need?" on a daily basis (and often throughout the day).** Often, people who turn to food to cope, and shame their bodies in the process, are in need of something – comfort, love, support, acceptance, etc. Find out what it is you truly need, and fulfill those needs. For example, if you need comfort after some heartbreaking news, give yourself a hug and tell yourself, in the kindest voice possible, that this, too, shall pass. If you chose to turn to food, offer compassion (over shame). You may continue to turn to food every once in a while when you are recovered. Offer yourself compassion when that does happen.

6. **Move your body for joy each day.** Give up the need to sweat it out at the gym every day if you don't enjoy that type of movement. The likelihood of consistently continuing movement that you don't enjoy is low. If you hate what you do, you won't feel joy and will move to shaming yourself for "not keeping up" on the days you miss. Moving your body in ways that bring you joy each day will allow you to keep it up, and you will feel good about yourself. There will be no shame on an off day.

7. **Take time for self-care every day.** Self-care isn't just about hot bubble baths and meditating, although those are great self-care activities! Self-care is also about saying no to something that does not align to your values, having a much needed (hard) conversation with someone and radically accepting what is. (Remember, you don't have to like what is. Simply accepting what is, sets you free.)

8. **Learn to let go and to forgive:** yourself and others. Holding grudges towards yourself and others keeps you in a cycle of resentment. Resentment chips away at your happiness. Forgive yourself for putting your body through all you have. Forgive yourself for buying into the diet industry and all its false promises. Forgive, forgive and forgive. It is truly a gift!

9. **Develop not just a morning meditation practice, but also a practice of checking in with your body for a couple minutes multiple times a day.** This practice helps you tune into your body and know what it will need at any given point (goes along with #5).

10. **Hire a coach in addition to your therapist.** A therapist will focus on what got you to where you are today and healing those

wounds. A coach will focus on where you want to be tomorrow. With a coach, it's about coming up with a plan to live out your life's dreams. Having a coach myself has allowed me to catapult *much* quicker toward my dreams, because my dreams become concrete goals. My coach is my accountability partner. She's my guide from the side. I wouldn't be where I am today without the coaches who have coached me along my journey.

11. **Prioritize yourself.** This is hard, especially for moms who typically put everyone else first. If you don't put on your own oxygen mask first, you won't be able to help anyone else, including yourself. It's okay to delegate, or simply de-prioritize, things that once used to be things that only you did.

12. **Find hobbies.** You are so much more than your titles of mom, wife, friend, sister, daughter, co-worker, leader, volunteer, etc. Finding hobbies allows you to have an outlet for enjoyment on the hard days when you don't think you can do it. You may even learn a thing or two about yourself through the process of a hobby too!

13. **Repeat this mantra on a daily basis: I AM ENOUGH!** There is no job, no amount of money and certainly no number on a scale that will prove your worth. You are worthy as you are, without all these "things" and titles.

14. **Throw away the scale!** There is so much harm in weighing yourself every day. In fact, I don't think you can overcome an eating disorder or body image issues when weighing yourself daily. That scale is not a measurement of your health or your worth. And when you go to the doctor's office, decline to be weighed unless it is necessary. Also, if a weight is needed, go on the scale backwards and ask that the person to not state the weight out loud.

15. **Get rid of "smaller" clothes.** There is no need to keep clothes that no longer fit in the hopes of fitting into them *someday*. This is a subtle way of your inner critic shaming you. Get yourself a few new outfits that you feel good in, no matter the size, and give away those that no longer fit.

16. **Advocate for yourself.** Find new providers if need be. Let them know that telling a person to diet is perpetuating the problem. Ask them to show you a sound study that shows people keep the weight off for more than five years when they diet. Remind them that weight cycling (going up and down in weight due to dieting) is

deadlier than being at the same "overweight" weight.

17. **Give yourself the utmost compassion you can.** This is important when overcoming a life-long cycle of shame. Society likes to tell you to be harsh on yourself to meet your goals, yet this proves to not work. Your body was shamed by you and others. Now is the time to offer your body, and your whole being, self-compassion. Instead of bashing yourself when you don't like something you did or the way your body looks on a particular day, offer yourself loving words and kindness. Go deep with curiosity in these moments, rather than the old stand-by of shame. Ask what could have triggered this? How can I respond to this with compassion?

18. **Follow positive social media accounts and let go of ones that are hindering you and your journey.** Do you notice yourself talking negatively about your body after seeing a friend post about her weight loss diet? Put her posts on mute (so they don't show up in your feed). Not everyone aligns with your views on weight loss (it's a societal pressure to be thin) and it's okay to put your own needs ahead of remaining "friends."

19. **Remember that your journey towards body acceptance and eating disorder recovery are not linear.** They are like the 1970's rotary dial phone cord. It will ebb and flow, even when you are in a recovered state. It's okay. It does not mean you have "failed" at recovery!

20. **Go out and live your life.** Stop waiting for *someday*. Someday is today. Today is the day you will start to live life to the fullest. Time on this earth is not guaranteed. Life is precious, and we must not wait until we are at some "ideal" weight to live it. Regrets happen when we wait for *someday*. Live life without that regret!

Author Update

I finished writing this memoir in December 2020. It sat collecting electronic dust until I was introduced to Krista, my editor and publishing consultant, in January 2022. We have been working together since April to publish this work of art for all of you, and I pinch myself thinking about my *someday* dream coming to life. I carefully considered the day to officially publish this work of art: October 27, 2022, the five-year anniversary of my diagnosis.

I still consider myself to be recovered to this day (August 2022), although some things on the outside have changed since December 2020. My daughter, Kaitlyn, graduated from college and recently moved out to start her special education teaching career in a small town near her former college. My son, Ian, is now living in an apartment near his college and in his third year of studying Math and Computer Science. All of this means that my husband and I are empty nesters, at least for the time being. (I say for the time being since the kids are early on in their adult lives and we don't know if moving home is still in the picture for either one.) We are working to redefine our relationship without the kids at home, which is an adjustment for sure. We have not yet travelled out of the state or country since that paradise trip to the Dominican Republic when the world was shutting down in March 2020. We have learned to enjoy simple pleasures at home in the meantime – walks with our faithful dog, Ollie, dinners at home with just the two of us, and sweet post-it notes to each other like we once did when first married 27 years ago. We hope to start travelling out of the state and country at some point in the future, yet I no longer see it as a yearly "must have" as I once did pre-Covid. At times, those simple pleasures at home are worth so much more to me. Covid taught me that a slower pace of life is okay and that I prefer that pace.

After having a heart scan completed in February 2021, I learned that I have calcium build-up on the left ventricle of my heart. At first, I thought this meant a death sentence like my dad. After the initial shock of the news, I decided to partner with a dietitian, Regina, at The Emily Program. I also chose to see my therapist, Kris, on a more frequent basis. I worked with Regina for 18 months, which allowed me to realize that I am okay and can simply go back to the basics I learned in my early treatment days and be just fine. A new health diagnosis does not mean another diet. It took a lot of work to convince myself (and truly believe it) that another diet was not needed with this diagnosis.

I worked with Regina to continue in my practice of Intuitive Eating, to incorporate more fruits and veggies to my meals, to reduce my stress, to consistently move my body in joyful ways, and to continue to heal my relationship with soda pop (yes, this was/is still haunting me at times). I realized that when I am engaging in emotional eating (or drinking Mtn Dew), it means I have some unmet need to address. Usually, it's that I need comfort, a nap, down time or a Dear Man conversation.

At my last appointment with Regina in early August 2022, I declared that I was still recovered and had been all along. Sometimes, we think a little slip-up of body shaming or comfort eating means a pattern of eating disorder behavior. It does not. I had to remind myself that recovery does not mean "no slips ups" for the rest of my life. That is the all-or-nothing mentality that no longer works for me. Each day, that reminder is needed.

I am still coaching people and obtained my ICF (International Coaching Federation) credential in January 2022. This had been a dream of mine for over four years! I am an ACC level coach now, which means I completed all the requirements necessary to be credentialed. This is a big deal and the closest thing to being certified in the coaching industry. At the writing of this update (August 2022), I am also awaiting to hear of my credential from Positive Intelligence® on being a PQ Certified Coach. I have completed all the trainings, coached clients through the introductory program, submitted all the paperwork and the client coaching sessions and am simply waiting to hear. I am sure I will have this credential by the time this book publishes.

I was able to move into a job I absolutely love (at the same employer I spoke about in this memoir) in January 2022. Until this change, I continued to work for the same boss, but with added scope, (the same boss I spoke about having Dear Man conversations with from Chapter 13). After nearly three years of working for him, I knew I wanted a true change in about May 2021. This was not anxiety provoked as you often read in my journal entries in my early days of treatment, but true authentic desire to pivot my career in the corporate world. I had healed so much that staying still in a job I no longer enjoyed was quite painful. It was affecting my mental health in a negative way. In November 2021, I had a conversation with my now boss. I scheduled time with her after it was suggested months earlier. I don't know why I dragged my feet on meeting with her (that might have been anxiety driven by the thought of trying a new career path). In our meeting, she told me about an opportunity she was going to post for Change Leadership, Communications and Training for a recent acquisition the organization had completed. I applied for the position and was hired by her! I still pinch myself thinking I was able to pivot my career and that she took a chance on me. We still have conversations here and there about this. I feel extremely grateful to have this job.

One of the reasons I love my current job is because it is focused on changes happening at the organizational level and helping coach people through the change itself. This aligns with what I do for my coaching practice, so that is probably why I love it so much. When coaching people in their personal lives, they are navigating a change as well. My leader supported my pursuit of formal change leadership training, and I proudly obtained my Change Management Practitioner credential with Prosci in August 2022.

While life on the outside has changed since 2020 when I finished writing my book, my inside core self has not. That is the beauty of spending years healing the emotional bruises from the inside out. You quiet the inner critic who says you are not good enough and you move toward a life you have been waiting to live *someday*. I can't tell you how freeing this feels! And the icing on the cake is that while all these new changes in my professional world are great, I am still grounded in the fact that they don't define me in any way. If you stripped them all away, I would still be the same Teresa Joan Schmitz that I was before achieving them.

Acknowledgements

First and foremost, I would like to thank all those who I have met along the way of my eating disorder recovery journey, especially who were battling their own demons too. We may have happened to share an eating disorder diagnosis, yet you all taught me so much more about LIVING! To my special friends, Stefania, Leanne and Kathryn – thanks for all the memories. I will never forget all the moments we shared inside and outside of treatment. You made me feel so surrounded by love and support throughout my journey in treatment. To Stefania, who continues to hold space for me each day by reaching out to ask what I need. This has been a profound experience for me. And to Leanne, who continues to carve out time amid her life to have a 5-hour long dinner with me still. To Rachel, who unfortunately lost her battle with her eating disorder in early 2021 – you taught me what it meant to love with all your heart. I will cherish those crazy socks you gifted me!

I'd like to thank those who hold a special place in my heart at The Emily Program – Kris Johnson, my therapist, and Regina, my dietitian. Spending countless hours with you in sessions has led me to become an even better version of me. Thank you for holding space for me, through tears and laughter both! A special shout out to Angie Michel, the producer of my *Peace Meal* podcast episode, which aired in August 2020. Her support, guidance and care of me through that process led me to gain a new friend! Thank you also for your foreword for this book. You have an amazing ability to positively impact people with your words. And a special thank you to Jillian Lampert, who interviewed me for my first ever podcast guest appearance on *Peace Meal*. Your genuine nature and kindness made me feel so at ease, even well after the recording stopped and we talked "life."

To all my former therapists and dietitians at The Emily Program – Miranda, Nicole, Abbie and Katherine. You held such a safe space for me, and I will be forever grateful for that. To Jen Nelson, our DBT skills instructor and IOP therapist at The Emily Program. Your words left an indelible mark on me, ones I won't ever forget (many of which are captured in this book as a way to spread your wisdom with the world). They are words that I use when empowering women in my own coaching practice today. Thank you for all you gifted us during programming. It's a gift that keeps on giving!

To my Body Image yoga therapist, Mary, and yoga instructor, Sarah, at The Emily Program. Thank you for allowing me the space to fall into my body and listen to what it is trying to tell me at any given moment of the day. Such a special talent you both have.

Thank you to Mari, who lovingly suggested that I seek out support from an eating disorder treatment facility like The Emily Program. You were so compassionate in your words and were the one who gently nudged me toward a life of freedom with recovery!

To my current gynecologist, Dr. Amy Kelly, at MN Women's Care in Woodbury. You were so kind to me when I first sat on the exam table in your room and cried as I shared what my prior gynecologist used to say to me about my weight and how she made me feel. I will never forget the tears in your own eyes as I shared this and your gentle voice telling me, "No one should ever have to feel that way at the doctor's," as you handed me the tissue box.

To Abby Wagstrom, my general practitioner. You are the first doctor who has treated me as a whole person, someone beyond the number on the scale. Your kindness has meant so much to me and is why I won't ever miss a doctor's appointment with you. In a health system full of weight bias, you have no idea how normal you make me feel.

To my hair stylist Steph, who makes me feel like a million dollars every time I see her. She has listened to me throughout my journey and is such a beacon of positivity.

Thank you to all my own coaching clients, past, current and future. You took a chance on me, some of you when I was first starting out, and I am forever thankful for your trust in me. You have all taught me something too.

To Ari, who designed my company logo. You took my idea of a woman with curves giving herself a big hug and brought it to life for me. You are an amazing and talented artist and leader. I cannot wait to see what transpires in your life. It's been a blessing to partner with you and to watch you grow!

Thank you to Melissa, the photographer who snapped my professional headshots for the back of my book, my website and my online social media platforms. Your willingness to trek all around downtown Hastings on a beautiful, yet windy, spring evening and allow for me to change outfits three different times, all in the name of capturing the "perfect" shot, was greatly appreciated!

Thank you to my book cover/back cover designer, Noel. You took the info and details from my book brief and brought my dreams to reality! You were super patient with me through all the edits I requested along the way. I was impressed by your thought process and couldn't wait to make my dream and your design into reality! For those wondering the thought process from the designer regarding the cover design, he told me that the balloon signifies my journey of overcoming my eating disorder. And that when I "eventually knew that the cake is not what hinders me from becoming what I wanted to be, I am able to bring the cake with me in my journey."

Thank you to my nearly lifelong friend, Heather. Your compassion on that day I chose to open up to you will never be forgotten. You held space for me to cry and supported me moving forward. You are a gift, and I am lucky enough to call you my friend. I look forward to all the new steps we will take together in this thing called life.

To my sister, Missy. Thank you for being there on the days when I doubted myself in the beginning and just before my recovery journey started. Allowing me to shed those tears meant a lot to me and still does. You and your family, including Brian, Amanda and Joe, mean the world to me. Life wouldn't be the same without you all in it. Thank you for showing up time and time again for me and my family.

To my mom and dad, who did their best in raising me to be the woman I am today. I am not resentful for anything that did or did not happen as a young child. You truly did the best you could in raising us girls. I feel honored to be your youngest daughter, your "little flower." You, Mom, my *prayer warrior*, have taught me to trust in the good Lord and watch Him deliver! I treasure our Sunday talks together in person each week.

To my friend, Shari, for allowing me to text non-stop during the working day when I was at the height of my eating disorder and you had no idea. Thank you for being there through all of our life and career journeys for over 15 years. It's been quite the ride and you continue to offer unwavering support.

To my friend, Christin, for listening with an open mind when I shared my story and why I was not the best leader when you reported to me. I am grateful that you saw something in me I didn't see in myself at the time and hung on until I got the help I needed.

To my friend, Karen, who shared many walks with me during my recovery journey when living across the street. I miss our walks and talks and treasure the times we can spend together when you are back in Minnesota.

To my friend, Toby, who provided such good coaching when I needed it most in those early days of wanting more out of life. She was such a patient coach. She also was the one who introduced me to Krista, my editor and my publisher guide. Thank you, Krista, for all your guidance and support throughout this publishing process. You are such a blessing to me in getting this work of art published! I could not have become a published author without your guidance.

To my fellow coaching colleagues. Delia, thank you for always sharing your knowledge, ideas and resources, along with your general love of life and others. You are such an inspiration! To Pam, who referred clients to me for my body acceptance group coaching. I will be forever grateful for the opportunities you sent my way. You hold a special place in my heart. To Ruth, who gave me a chance at group coaching and introduced me to a larger network. To Tiffine (Coach T), who knows just when I need her encouragement the most. Praying with you at the end of our calls always brings me peace. To

Cathy, who mentored me on my ICF credential process, and Judy, who mentored me early on in my business. Both of you are inspirational coaches and business owners. To all the other IIT coaches I had a chance to work with not already mentioned– Alan, Tina, Renee, Naomi, Mara, Angela, and Silvia. Watching you in action taught me so much!

To all my current and former managers in the corporate world. You each taught me something along the way. Some of you saw me at my worst, yet had no idea what was going on at the time. When you told me, "You're too hard on yourself," you had no idea how much inner criticism was going on during and after this comment.

To my faithful four-legged friend, Ollie. I kicked and screamed getting you when you were a 10-week-old puppy, and now I could not imagine life without you. You give me reason to move my body for pure joy each day. You show me how important unconditional love truly is.

Last, and most important, thank you to my loving husband Dale, and our two beautiful children, Kaitlyn and Ian. You allowed me the time and space needed to heal, which meant you had to step up and fill in when I was in IOP and focused on my treatment. You have each walked beside me and never doubted me, even on my worst days. You have supported all that I have sought to do with this new-found freedom called recovery, which includes the writing of this book, launching my coaching practice and finding new hobbies. I love you more than words can say.

Praise for *It Was Never About the Cake:*

"This is a story that needs to be told because it needs to be heard. In its beauty it holds and offers grit, truth and hope to those struggling, seeking, learning, supporting, and recovering. It wholeheartedly speaks what is so needed to be heard – you are not alone."

—Dr. Jillian Lampert, Chief Strategy Officer, The Emily Program and Veritas Collaborative, but more importantly, a mom, partner, friend, recovered person, and more

"For too long, people with eating disorders lacked models of midlife recovery. That has changed with Teresa's open and generous book. In it, she shares the challenges of diagnosis of an eating disorder at age 46. Teresa's story shows how eating disorders affect people of all ages and are not about food or weight. Teresa's journey of discovery and recovery will be an inspiration to many. Kudos, Teresa!"

—Heidi J. Dalzell, PsyD, Licensed Psychologist and Specialist in Midlife Eating Disorders

"Teresa Schmitz courageously tackles an issue that's both common and rarely discussed: eating disorders at a "certain" age. In beautifully sharing her own challenging journey – with relatable details and feelings – Teresa reminds all women everywhere that it's critical to be honest about our battles...and our pain. By doing so, we can begin to heal ourselves in a way that is healthy and sustaining. I believe this book will indeed reach women who most need to read these words...helping them to know they're not alone."

—Karla Hult, Journalist and Founder of So Many Goodbyes

"Teresa Schmitz sheds light on the little-known narrative that eating disorders can and do occur in older adults. Even though anecdotal and quantitative evidence shows otherwise, it is the commonly accepted stereotype that eating disorders only affect those in young, thin, white, female bodies; however, It Was Never About the Cake helps challenge that. As an expert on Fatphobia and weight stigma, specifically within the eating disorder world, I'm incredibly proud to see this story told and in the hands of people who, like Teresa, are looking for a story that resonates with them and their experiences. Schmitz imparts a deep and vulnerable wisdom, filling a literary gap and providing a progressive and accurate portrayal of the struggles and hardships that an eating disorder causes – and the joys that recovery from it can foster."

—Serena Nangia, Founder, The Body Activists, thebodyactivists.com

"The antidote to judgement is curiosity." Teresa is the embodiment of this quote. Throughout her recovery journey, Teresa continuously turned towards curiosity as a way to quiet or challenge judgement when it arrived. Whether she wore silly socks because it felt uncomfortable or she asked her self why patterns, behaviors or thoughts existed, Teresa worked on suspending judgement and allowing things to be as they are. When we are curious about what is, we continue to explore. We open ourselves to places we never knew existed. When we judge, we stop exactly where we are."

— Jen Nelson, LPCC

"I remember the day when Teresa first walked into my office: March 1, 2017. I saw a woman with a beautiful smile but a very hopeless look in her eyes. She was filled with shame about her lack of "willpower" and body hatred. She said that she "acted happy on the outside, but she was truly not happy." Food had become her hidden secret and her tormentor! She had worked so hard to find the right "diet" to make her thin enough so she would not hate her body. "I'm not worth anything because of my weight." She knew her body hatred was helping to fuel the cycle of secretive eating, and then being ashamed, but did not know what to do. We talked about her relationship to food, the need to stop "diets" and move forward in learning to love her body, herself and food. In October 2017 she was ready to attend The Emily Program. She was so happy and at peace with her decision. I was so proud of how far she had come to get to this point.

Over the years, I had often wondered how she was doing and silently praying that she discovered a new love for herself. When I received her wonderful email this past year, I was filled with such joy! She discovered a love and acceptance for herself!

Teresa's journey needs to be told, and I am beyond thrilled that she is sharing her life and healing as a help to others who struggle in their relationship with food. She has truly learned to LOVE herself just as she is! Bless you, Teresa!"

—Mari Boyd, MA, LMFT, Licensed Marriage & Family Therapist, www.Mariboydcounseling.com

Individual (1:1) and Group Coaching Testimonials:

"Teresa knew how to get to the heart quickly; she helped sort things out and put me into action. She knew what to ask and at the right time for processing to get to the point. I was very thankful for her kind, caring and easy-to-talk-to manner. She is an amazing and encouraging safe-haven. Coaching with Teresa was a great experience, and I plan to use her masterful coaching services again. Teresa, you are awesome and a true blessing."

"Teresa, you are an incredible coach, who listens so well, understands what each individual is going through and you have this ability to put everyone at ease and allow them to feel the feels, stay connected and no longer feel alone!"

"When I first started meeting with Teresa, my main goal was to gain the confidence needed to become a better leader and wasn't really sure what I needed to work on aside from that. Fast forward a year into meeting with Teresa, and I can honestly say that not only has my leadership confidence skyrocketed, but I have greatly improved my self-awareness, mindfulness and overall understanding of myself. During our sessions, she carefully listens to what I have to say and somehow always comes up with the right questions that make me dig deeper into an issue or see it in a different light.

Before our first session, I was under the impression that I would just learn some new strategies and tips to help me increase my confidence and become a better leader. I thought maybe there was a magical "list" of things that all good leaders do and it was the same for everyone. However, I quickly learned that the first step to increasing my confidence was to understand myself both professionally AND personally. Teresa helped me discover things deep within myself that I had no idea were contributing to my confidence levels and ability to show up as my authentic self. She helped me recognize, understand and stand up to my inner critic by sharing extremely helpful resources and suggesting new strategies I could practice in my daily life. By understanding what was getting in the way of my confidence, I was able to start addressing it and working with Teresa to come up with ways to move past it.

Overall, our coaching sessions have given me the confidence to show up as an effective leader and peer at work *and* the mindfulness needed to navigate difficult situations at work and in my personal life."

"Teresa is an extremely conscientious and compassionate coach. She consistently provides a warm, trusting space to explore beyond your 'comfort zone'. Teresa further reaffirms a high level of respect, care and confidentiality in every session. In a group coaching dynamic, I've witnessed her display graceful leadership and clearly summarize others' perspectives with sensitivity and insight. She sets the right tone to allow for deeper sharing and connection. I would jump at the chance to work with Teresa in both a one-on-one and a group setting."

"I started coaching with Teresa in November 2019. Since I started coaching, Teresa has given me the tools to help me as I navigate my journey. She's helped me problem solve, navigate the challenges that can arise, talk through what is and isn't working and determine the steps I need to take in order to make it happen!

Because of coaching, I have learned to make myself a priority and be able to say "no" to things that are not going to fill my cup. Teresa is the reason I feel confident I will be able to achieve my big audacious career goals. She has helped me make a plan and what my next five years might look like.

Coaching has been the best decision I have made. It fills my cup each month. If you are thinking about coaching, I would highly recommend checking out Teresa. She is wonderful to work with, caring and very knowledgeable!"

"Teresa established rapport very well. She demonstrated an interest that made me feel heard and cared about. She inspired me to pursue my goals and brought me greater clarity and understanding."

Testimonials from the 12-week Positive Intelligence®
PQ Mental Fitness Group Coaching Circle:

"I'm much more aware of my saboteurs and have made active attempts to bring my sage to the forefront. This makes me generally a bit less anxious and stressed. I breathe before I tackle tough issues."

"My self-compassion changed because my understanding changed, and that was so powerful!"

"I feel I have more empathy towards myself."

"I really enjoyed this opportunity. My self-discovery over these last weeks was so powerful and will be long lasting. I am grateful for Teresa and this course."

"This program has forced me to develop myself in ways I haven't imagined before. You take ownership and responsibility in what you get out of this program by how much you put into it. I have learned when I am slipping into my Saboteur mode with negative emotions and mindset, and I have been able to pull myself out of those negative feelings and into a positive Sage mood much quicker than before. Working within a pod or completing this course with a friend helps with accountability when your Saboteurs take over and you lack motivation. Your peers can help pick you up and push you to continue growing yourself alongside of them. While taking this course, I was able to apply my learnings immediately and could see a shift in mindset almost instantly. I highly recommend taking this course if you are looking to improve your point of view on life in both work and at home."

"I took this course without much background information regarding Saboteurs and Sage. What a great opportunity for myself to realize what is going on in my mind, how to allow it, listen to it, and then work around it. Personally, it moved me towards self-compassion for myself, and also a huge amount of self-discovery. I have always enjoyed learning the 'reasons why' in life, and this was very powerful for me. I am able to transfer this incredible knowledge personally and professionally moving forward. This newfound knowledge will not only help me, but will also help me deal with others. I am truly grateful for this course and highly recommend it to anyone!"

"This program opened my eyes on how judgmental I was and how I reacted to those judgements, including myself. I have been working on that and only one of the Saboteurs. I feel this has changed my outlook towards others, including family. I also loved the quiet PQ reps led by Shirzad, as they tended to focus me and take a break from things in which the Saboteurs were showing through."

Recommended Resources

Websites:

www.emilyprogram.com
www.nationaleatingdisorders.org
www.theprojectheal.org
https://self-compassion.org

Books:

Intuitive Eating by Evelyn Tribole, MS, RDN & Elyse Resch, MS, RDN
Self-Compassion by Kristin Neff. PhD
Anti-Diet by Christy Harrison
This Is Me by Chrissy Metz
Atlas of the Heart by Brené Brown, PhD, MSW
The Gifts of Imperfection by Brené Brown, PhD, MSW
Healing Your Emotional Self by Beverly Engel
The Body Keeps the Score by Bessel van der Kolk, M.D.
It Will Never Happen to Me by Claudia Black, PhD
Brave Enough by Jessie Diggins

Workbooks:

The Intuitive Eating Workbook by Evelyn Tribole, MS, RDN & Elyse Resch, MS, RDN
The Mindful Self-Compassion Workbook by Kristin Neff, PhD and Christopher Germer, PhD
The Body Image Workbook by Thomas Cash, PhD
The Food & Feelings Workbook by Karen R. Koenig, LCSW, M.Ed

Podcasts:

Peace Meal hosted by The Emily Program
Behind the Bite hosted by Dr. Cristina Castagnini
Recovery Bites hosted by Karin Lewis

About the Author

After her recovery from an eating disorder diagnosis at mid-life, author and certified coach Teresa Schmitz started her own coaching practice focused on empowering women. Teresa coaches women to rediscover their happiness by showing up authentically and loving themselves unconditionally, no matter their size. Compelled to change how we view ourselves and our bodies, Teresa started her practice with the goal of empowering others to feel like she did after recovery. Teresa would say, "I discovered My Best Self Yet!" Thus, her company My Best Self Yet, LLC, was launched.

During the pandemic, Teresa and several other certified coaches co-founded and formed a group coaching program called "In It Together." This program specialized in using your character strengths in times of uncertainty. Along with her coaching work, Teresa has worked for major U.S. corporations in senior management, focusing on communications, change management, project management, and training.

Teresa enjoys speaking, writing and blogging on the topic of overcoming body image issues and empowering others to discover their best selves yet! She enjoys traveling with her husband Dale, walking her Goldendoodle, journaling, and spending time with her two beautiful adult children Kaitlyn and Ian.

Learn more at **MyBestSelfYet.com**.

Looking for a compassionate, experienced speaker for your event? Need a knowledgeable guest for your podcast or show? Teresa is available to share her journey of overcoming an eating disorder and body image issues with others, both virtually and in person.

Speaking topics include:

- Her personal story/journey
- The power of overcoming significant hurdles at mid-life so as to become who you were meant to be
- The importance of self-care (the art of putting on your own oxygen mask first)
- Defining success on your own terms to increase your happiness
- Developing a positive mindset by focusing on your mental fitness
- Empathy – the key to building a lasting relationship with yourself and those around you
- Her *It Was Never About the Cake* book

If you would like to collaborate to build a custom topic for a podcast or other speaking event, please let Teresa know. There is power in collaborating and making something unique for your audience! Links to previous podcasts interviews:

Eating Disorder at Midlife: **https://bit.ly/3xR1JPP**

Weight Loss Treatment: **https://bit.ly/3KftW5j**

Teresa appeared on the Recovery Bites podcast with Karin Lewis: **https://karinlewisedc.com/podcast/episode120**

For any and all speaking and writing requests, please contact Teresa at:
MyBestSelfYet.com/contact/

While Teresa would love to speak to your group, she is equally passionate about writing for your audience too (guest blog post or article). Below are a few samples of guest blogs posts she has written for The Emily Program and Project Heal:

Eating Disorders Do Happen Over Age 40: **https://bit.ly/3KozR85**

How Coping with Another Diagnosis is a Big Deal in Recovery: **https://bit.ly/3vOEza0**

Traditions: **https://bit.ly/36SX3Ok**

Outgrowing ED's Clothes: **https://bit.ly/3kdZFsX**

Written from the Heart: **https://bit.ly/3KdgbUM**

Choosing to Say Yes to Treatment: **https://bit.ly/3rVpyCd**

Putting in the Work: **https://bit.ly/3ENzdzY**

For any and all speaking and writing requests, please contact Teresa at:
MyBestSelfYet.com/contact/

MyBestSelfYet.com

Teresa Schmitz is an ICF (International Coaching Federation) certified ACC level coach offering group and private 1:1 coaching. If you would like to explore whether she is the right life coach for you, sign up now for a free 60-minute discovery call. Visit Teresa's calendar link on her website under the1:1 Coaching section at: **https://MyBestSelfYet.com/services/**

Do you want to quiet your inner critic and reach your fullest potential? Teresa offers the **Positive Intelligence**® PQ Mental Fitness program to coaching clients. Read more about this PQ Mental Fitness offering at **mybestselfyet.com/1466-2.**

Review all of her current services at: **MyBestSelfYet.com/services**

Follow Teresa on social media:

Instagram: **www.instagram.com/my.best.self.yet**
Facebook: **www.facebook.com/MyBestSelfYet**
LinkedIn: **www.linkedin.com/in/teresaschmitz**

Request to join Teresa's private Facebook Group called "Body Acceptance for Middle Aged Women." It's a group for middle aged women who want to be surrounded by others journeying towards self- and body acceptance and ditching diet culture. Join now at:

www.facebook.com/groups/743357746695957

Sign-up to receive alerts about new blog posts at **MyBestSelfYet.com** (at the bottom of the Home page or Blog page).

Freebies:

If you would like to receive 30 days of journal prompts, go to: **https://bit.ly/3OEEWwA**

If you'd like to try the Values Exercise from chapter 8, visit: **https://bit.ly/3Kiw9gy**

Do the 2-minute Mirror Exercise. Access it here: **https://bit.ly/3OEqJQo**

Continue to check out Teresa's social media and website in the months and years to come for updates, additional offerings and free resources.

"If anything, I have learned through my healing journey that most things in life are a process and a journey – ever changing as time and people change."
—Teresa Schmitz

Printed in Great Britain
by Amazon

40965343R00116